individual. Of particular help to the reader will be the thirty-four illustrative clinical photographs.

A sympathetic exploration of sexual errors, this book will be of value to the clinical psychologist, counselor, counseling clergyman, educator, and physician. Characteristic of the study is the author's concern for and concentration on the individual, who must find a way to meet his physical difficulties on his own terms. For the layman the study of sexual handicaps serves as a healthy corrective to the old-time Puritanism that tends to equate modern sex education with moral restraint.

John Money is Associate Professor of Medical Psychology and Pediatrics in the Department of Psychiatry and Behavioral Sciences and the Department of Pediatrics, The Johns Hopkins University School of Medicine and Hospital. In 1956 he was a corecipient of the Hofheimer Prize of the American Psychiatric Association for distinguished research in hermaphroditism. In 1966 he received the Gold Medal Award of the Children's Hospital of Philadelphia for his contributions to the medical psychology of sex. In addition to being the author of over a hundred articles dealing with sexual anomalies, behavior genetics, psychoendocrinology, and reading problems, Professor Money is the editor and author of *Sex Research: New Developments, Reading Disability,* and *The Disabled Reader.*

Sex Errors of the Body

Dilemmas, Education, Counseling

SEX ERRORS
OF THE BODY

Dilemmas, Education, Counseling

By JOHN MONEY

Associate Professor of Medical Psychology and Pediatrics

Department of Psychiatry and Behavioral Sciences

and Department of Pediatrics, The Johns Hopkins University

The Johns Hopkins Press: Baltimore

Dedicated to the Memory of

Ruth Mary Money,

for the Generation Leaving,

and to the Memory of

David Childs Walker,

for the Generation Ahead

Preface

History sometimes dictates her own timetable for the affairs of men. Thus, it has not been until the decade of the sixties that society has been made ready to plan and discuss the sex education of its children and youth as a community responsibility. In the past, the need was not lacking—only its fulfillment. Now it seems destined that the sixties will be remembered as, among other things, the decade when sex education finally became liberalized and widely available. This greater availability of sexual information is part of a more extensive change in sexual mores which is often thought of as a sexual revolution in reaction to the taboos and prudery of Victorianism. The sexual revolution is, however, part of a tide of history that has been running for a longer period of time, contemporaneously with the larger tide of social change characteristic of our civilization, at least since the Renaissance and Reformation.

The era of the Reformation showed with particular vividness the clash between antithetical systems of sexual values. Puritanism and the Inquisition both represented negativism toward sex and upheld the virtues of a regulated, authoritarian, agrarian, and medieval society. Under the Inquisition, the antisex forces reached a climax of horror, torture, and death seldom paralleled in Western history. At the same time, the great courts of the rulers of Europe represented an attitude of tolerance toward sex with a degree of personal freedom, even licentiousness, that was predicated on social privilege and wealth—the wealth to support one's activities and maybe one's partners and offspring. The customs of the aristocracy prestigiously set the fashion for the less privileged to aspire toward. It was to be some time, however, after the fall of aristocratic privilege during the French Revolution, before aristocratic ideals of sexual freedom could be put into practice by the common man. Meantime, there would be the ambivalent era of the two-faced nineteenth century in which Puritanism and prudery vied with pornography and genteel vice—much as prohibition vies with bootlegging in parts of the South in the U.S. today.

The ambivalence of the nineteenth century persisted into the twentieth and might have continued in a state of equilibrium, except that the industrial revolution was to make its contribution to sex which would, in effect, initiate the contraceptive revolution—the perfection of a cheap, widely distributed, and erotically satisfactory contraceptive: the rubber condom. There had been other crude forms of contraception before, but the latex process for manufacturing the thin rubber sheath belongs to the 1920's.

It took from early in the century until after World War II before the public faced its responsibility of providing itself with superhighways on which to run the automobiles that its industry was producing. The time lag in deciding how to use contraceptives, today more varied than in the twenties and made even more effective with the Pill, is roughly comparable.

In the flapper age of the 1920's, birth control was for the upper classes and the educated. Their sons and daughters began revising their sexual customs, to include contraceptively safe sexual relations outside marriage. As a matter of public and legal policy, society was completely at odds with itself over whether it would accept birth control, even in marriage. People themselves made up society's mind for it. Married and unmarried alike, they went on practicing birth control, tasting some of that personal freedom in sexual decisions that had once been a privilege of the aristocratic and wealthy.

Personal freedom in sex is not the same as promiscuity. The postwar teenaged generation established this principle very clearly when its response to the contraceptive revolution was to invent the social institution of going steady. Today in the sixties, there is less rigidity about the obligation of getting engaged and married to the person with whom one is going steady. It is more acceptable to go steady for only as long as the bond of affection and sex keeps both partners together. The old moral values, including the double standard, have by no means disappeared. Nonetheless, the generation of the sexual revolution is quietly redefining for all adolescents, not only the aristocratic and wealthy, a new moral standard of personal freedom in sex in the era of universal contraception and population control.

Personal freedom in sex requires knowledge. Without knowledge, one can all too easily become trapped, unnecessarily and unwittingly, by remediable defects or faults in oneself or one's relationships. Knowledge requires teachers. Teachers require books—for which reason this book has been written. It is directed not only to the specialist, but also to the reader who is a layman in the field of sex education and has a responsible interest in the subject. The interest may be self-interest. In that case, there will be only a few readers with problems which they can identify between these covers. Nonetheless, by learning the extremes of what can happen in the morphology and function of sex, they will enhance their appreciation of their own normalcy.

The reader who is engaged professionally in sex education and counseling, whether he be school teacher, doctor, pastor, social worker, psychologist, marriage counselor, or whatever, will find his effectiveness greatly increased by knowing of the disorders discussed herein, as sooner or later he will come across some of them in real life. They are not exceptionally rare. He will come across other sexual disorders also, notably the psychosexual disorders. They constitute the material for a companion volume not yet written.

Acknowledgments

The author is supported by Research Career Development Award 2-K3-HD-18635, and Research Grant 5-RD1-HD-00325, from the Institute of Child Health and Human Development, United States Public Health Service. He was formerly supported by a grant from the Josiah Macy, Jr. Foundation. He also wishes to acknowledge gifts and grants from the Erickson Educational Foundation, the Henry Foundation, The Stiles E. Tuttle Trust, Mrs. Marion Colwill and Dr. and Mrs. Hershel Herzog.

The following people kindly provided illustrations from their files: Dr. Digamber Borgaonkar, Johns Hopkins University (Figs. 1 and 2); Dr. E. Philip Welch, Dalhousie University (Plate 2); Dr. Friedmund Neumann, Schering AG, West Berlin (Plate 8A); and Drs. Robert Goy and Charles Phoenix, Oregon Regional Primate Center (Plate 9). The clinical photography is from the medical photographic service at Johns Hopkins (Chester F. Reather, director) with special service rendered by Mrs. Mary Cochrane, Mr. James Todesco, and Mr. J. Lindsay Burch. Plate 8B is reproduced by the courtesy of Drs. F. Neumann and W. Elger from *Endokrinologie,* 50 (1966), 221.

The manuscript was typed by Miss Marcia Kelley. The book was edited by Mrs. Martha Bluming and designed by Mr. Gerard Valerio.

Contents

SEX ERRORS OF THE BODY

Dilemmas, Education, Counseling

Chapter One: Introduction

Most discussions and writings on sex education are formulated as though every American were named John Doe or Mary Smith. The same message is then assumed to be sufficient in the sex education of all the John Does and Mary Smiths. Yet everyone knows that this assumption is not valid. Each person is a special individual, unique in his own personality and life situation—and unique also, perhaps, in his own special problems and needs in sex education. The withdrawn, shy adolescent boy, born with a deformed penis that needed multiple surgical procedures for repair during childhood, will require encouragement even to rehearse in imagination the realistic possibility of exposing himself to sexual intercourse. Far less attention will be given to moral prohibition in his sex education than in that of the promiscuous delinquent who will try anything once (or more often) for money and will ruthlessly exploit his sexual resources.

In terms of active manpower, it is not feasible to give all sex education on a person-to-person basis. Parents might be expected to do it. They teach their infants the language, and much else besides, on this basis. But most parents are incapable of sufficiently disengaging themselves emotionally to receive their children's sexual confidences, especially in adolescence. Conversely, most children, sensing the taboos, withhold their most intimate questions and concerns. A prime source of difficulty is that, whereas total frankness on the child's part really deserves total frankness from the parents in return, in our sexually secretive and litigious society today,

5

most parents cannot and will not reveal all the details of their sexual histories to their children. It is tacitly agreed that there is a silent world of privacy governed by the fifth amendment.

In many cases a parent or child will also have been silenced on sexual topics by having nothing more than a locker room argot or a private euphemistic idiom with which to express himself. An essential part of an impartial outsider's skill is the ability to ascertain these terms and comfortably use them. He may blend them with his own erudite idiom, so that his listener may become proficient in the new vocabulary should he choose. It is a legacy of society's long history of sexual hypocrisy that the common words of sex, usually Anglo-Saxon in origin, have been outlawed as vulgar and dirty and replaced in polite society by Latinisms that still, today, seem highbrow and phony instead of homely and familiar to the majority of people. The four-letter words will perhaps one day become rehabilitated into universal respectability. Meantime, for millions of the not-so-literate public, colloquial idiom is the only one in which they feel at ease when talking. For them, the sex educator will adjust his own preferred language in order to hear the story "straight" and avoid all possible chances of misunderstanding based on ambiguities, euphemisms, and guessed meanings. For example, it is useless to talk about a clitoris to a girl who has not learned to identify this organ by any name; and it is awkwardly stilted to talk about ejaculating to a boy whose usage is always "discharging" or "coming."

Since there are limits to parental impartiality in sex education, an impartial outsider is a clear necessity. To serve as wide an audience as possible, this specialist will be obliged to convey the nucleus of a system of sex information to all comers assembled in large groups. Thereafter, it will be necessary to individualize sex education by providing opportunities for individual consultation and counseling. In this way the special needs of special cases will be identified and met.

Sometimes these special needs will be found to be predominantly psychosexual in character—as in emergent homosexuality, panic as a sequel to incest, inhibition and potential frigidity as a sequel to contact with a sexual prowler, and so forth. At other times, special individual needs will be predominantly morphologic or somatic in character. In some instances, it will be diagnostically clear that these needs are also somatic in origin, whereas others will belong in the gray zone of psychosomatic overlap in which a somatic symptom is psychosomatically ambiguous in origin, according to today's diagnostic techniques.

The remainder of this volume is concerned chiefly with conditions of a morphologic and somatic nature that create special problems of sex education. By and large, each of these conditions is rare, but cumulatively they occur frequently enough that the sex educator needs to be informed on how to deal with such as may arise. Traditionally, no one else, not even the physician, has been trained to meet these exigencies, so the responsible person with a trained interest in sex education can perform a very important service here. Moreover, the study of sexual deformities and handicaps serves as a healthy corrective to that insidious influence of old-time Puritanism which tends to equate modern sex education with moral restraint. Rather, one should be reminded that healthy sexual functioning is a delicately perfected and very positive achievement to be joyously celebrated.

Chapter Two: Developmental Sequence

The ultimate aim of sex education is the development of a child capable of healthy sexual and reproductive functioning in adulthood. Sex education thus fits into a sequence of developmental steps, the orderly progression of which is prerequisite to normal sexual functioning. In normal development, each step follows the other in such logical progression that one does not think of them as possibly being independent of one another. It was only through the study of sexual anomalies in which the sequence of development is not as expected (such as I have paid attention to over the past fifteen years), that it became possible to differentiate one step from another and identify the developmental variables of sex which may be independent of one another. One may list these variables as follows:

1. Genetic or chromosomal sex
2. Gonadal sex
3. Fetal hormonal sex
4. Internal morphologic sex
5. External morphologic sex
6. Hypothalamic sex
7. Sex of assignment and rearing
8. Pubertal hormonal sex
9. Gender identity and role
10. Procreative sex impairments

Each of these variables of development has its own probabilities of error or malfunction. Some of the errors overlap from one variable to another. One does not say that an anomaly is caused by a particular variable, because the cause is actually much more complicated than that and usually is a chain of events. Thus, a genetic error may lead to an error in the production of fetal hormones or an error in their use, which in turn leads to an error of sex-organ morphology, and so forth. For this reason, the principle of classification in what follows is a temporal and not a causal one. The different clinical anomalies are arranged according to the time in the developmental sequence of the variables of sex when the most prominent characteristics of the anomaly are set. This arrangement allows for overlap in problems of sex education, such as the issue of predicted sterility, incongruity between gender identity and other variables, transmissible genetic defect, and so on, for these problems are not determined by the origin of an anomaly, per se. For this reason there are frequent cross references in the text.

Chapter Three: Sex-Chromosomal Anomalies

The sex of a baby is normally determined by the X chromosome in the egg formed in the mother's ovary and the presence of another X chromosome or a Y in the fertilizing sperm from the father. Either an X or a Y could have been received when the sperm was formed in the testicle. A girl results when two Xs meet (Fig. 1), and a boy, when the combination is XY (Fig. 2).

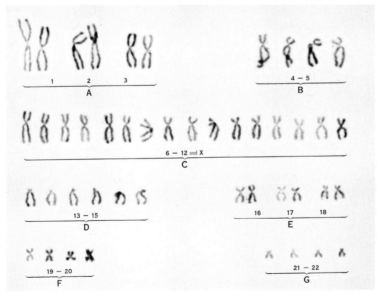

Fig. 1.—Female chromosomal karyotype showing two X chromosomes in Group C.

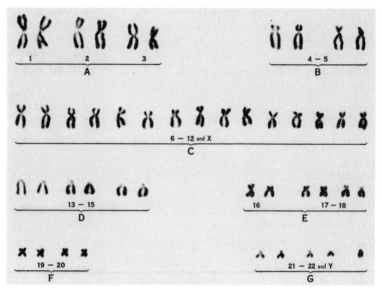

Fig. 2.—Male chromosomal karyotype showing one X chromosome in Group C and the Y chromosome in Group G.

It is possible for a fertilized egg to carry the wrong combination of sex chromosomes, the error having taken place either before fertilization or immediately after, in the earliest phases of cell division. Some of these errors will not produce any adverse effects, direct or indirect, and so will be discovered, if at all, only by chance.

Triple-X Syndrome

The triple-X syndrome in a female is an example of error (Plate 1). In this condition there are three X chromosomes (or even more) so that the total chromosome count is 47 (44 + XXX) instead of 46 (44 + XX). Some women with this condition are mentally retarded and so are discovered in chromosome surveys of institutions. Others are mentally normal, married, childbearing, and peacefully unaware of the chromosomal peculiarity of every cell of their bodies.

XYY Syndrome

There is a newly discovered anomaly in men (Plate 2) of an extra Y chromosome (44 + XYY). The first men discovered to have this condition were all in custody for undisciplined be-

16

havior, so there is a chance that the extra Y chromosome effects an adverse influence on subsequent behavior. In any case, at least some of these males will, as youths, present a special problem to the sex educator because of their delinquent acting-out.

Klinefelter's (XXY) Syndrome

In another condition of sex-chromosomal abnormality the adverse effects are more extensive. This is Klinefelter's syndrome (Plate 3). It is characterized by an extra X chromosome (44 + XXY)—or by more than one extra X—in a person who is male in sexual morphology. XXY males have a small penis, small testes, and are sterile. Typically, they are tall and skinny, with gangling legs and arms, though a few become obese. Some of them develop breast growth at puberty, so that their chests look feminine, like a girl in early adolescence. The masculine secondary sexual characteristics are usually weakly developed and do not respond to treatment with male sex hormone. Mentally, males with Klinefelter's syndrome are peculiar people. They seem to have a special, nonspecific proneness to mental impairment ranging all the way from gross mental deficiency to schizophrenia. A large number of them, if not all, who are not more severely afflicted, have what may best be characterized as an inadequate personality. Though they are typically very low-powered in sexual drive, paradoxically many of them manifest psychosexual behavior disorders.

The sex education problem with Klinefelter's syndrome may not become evident until adulthood when a work-up for infertility leads to the diagnosis. In other cases the diagnosis will be made much earlier in life, usually on the basis of physical findings at puberty. Then the task is not simply one of counseling for sterility (see p. 20.) It is usually a much greater task of counseling or psychotherapy relative to the over-all problems of psychopathology and life adjustment by which the individual is affected.

The sterility issue in older men may give rise to a special problem when the diagnosis of Klinefelter's syndrome (or any other proven cause of sterility) is not established until after they are married. Some such individuals firmly believe that they are not sterile and offer the evidence of a family to prove it.

In these cases it is wise to allow that there are exceptions to all known rules. It is none of the business of a professional outsider to be the agent of a family break-up, by implying a wife's infidelity, however justified his suspicions.

There are some men and boys who, when they learn of the probability of their own infertility, deliberately elect not to be told the final result of a sperm count or a testicular biopsy done as a test of fertility. These are people who have been told of artificial or donor insemination from a "sperm bank." They choose to live with an element of uncertainty so that, if they should eventually resort to donor insemination, either partner may never be quite sure whose sperm fertilized the egg.

It is an individual matter for an infertile man to decide between adoption or donor insemination. My own preference is to recommend donor insemination, since it permits the woman to undergo the biological experience of pregnancy. It also permits secrecy regarding the husband's sterility, should that happen to be important. I know of one case where a young man was able to create an illusion of paternity for even his own mother to believe.

A man's decision in favor of donor insemination, rather than adoption, must be made in collaboration with his wife. Both must be in agreement. Often they need counseling together, in order to reach full agreement. A husband may, for instance, feel that he will consider a child by donor insemination to be hers alone, the parenthood unshared. Conversely, a wife may have a secret fear that her husband may have no allegiance to the child, may resent her for having borne it, and may too easily leave her, breaking up the marriage later on. In some cases there may be a religious and moral issue to be worked through.

Counseling includes, for some couples, the reassurance of knowing exactly what are the practicalities of donor insemination. They want to know to whom to apply, how the program is carried out technically, what safeguards are taken to ensure that the donor's identity will never be revealed to them, nor theirs to him, and what they may expect regarding the physical appearance of the child. The answers require familiarity with local facilities on the part of the counselor. The program, from initial application to conception, varies in detail from place to place. My usual recommendation is to apply to the fertility clinic of a large medical center, for the anonymity it provides.

Though male sterility can sometimes be predicted with certainty during boyhood, its earliest discovery is more likely to be at the time of puberty. Almost all young adolescent boys, I have found, appreciate not having the information withheld. They worry more when left to make their own un-certain inferences, too afraid to express them, and unsupported emotionally by a more knowledgeable adult. They benefit by knowing that infertility does not imply either impotence or an inability to marry, but only the need to have a family by either adoption or donor insemination. They can be told in such a way (see p. 20) that the information causes least hurt and prepares them to cope with having to tell a prospective spouse about themselves when the time comes (see p. 33).

Turner's (XO) Syndrome

Another chromosomal anomaly with many body effects is Turner's syndrome (Plate 4). The basic genetic defect is that one chromosome is missing, the remaining one being always an X, so that the total is only 45 (44 + XO). There are several variants of this syndrome in one of which the second X chromosome may be present, but with one of its arms broken (a deletion chromosome). In another variant, the so-called mosaic, some cells of the body are XX and some XO; and there are other mosaics also.

The two pathognomonic symptoms of Turner's syndrome are absence of the ovaries (gonadal agenesis or dysgenesis) and short stature in a person with the body morphology of a girl. Should an exploratory operation be performed, the ovaries look like streaks instead of being round and plump. They make neither eggs nor female sex hormones. The affected person will, therefore, be sterile and will remain sexually in-fantile in appearance until treated with female sex hormones (Plate 5), which also produce menstruation.

The genetic defect in Turner's syndrome is associated with many other impairments which may or may not occur in a given individual. These deformities include webbed neck, webbed fingers and toes, small receding chin, pigmented moles, epicanthal folds (resembling those of oriental eyes), blue-baby and other heart defects, kidney and ureter defects, hearing loss, and, in cognitional functioning, space-form perceptual deficit, directional-sense deficit, and motor clumsiness.

Psychologically, girls with Turner's syndrome have an unusual capacity to deal with stress and adversity. They usually cope well with the problems consequent on their condition. Psychosexually, they are the epitome of femininity and very maternal in their play and child-care interests from infancy onward. This femininity and maternalism may, conceivably, be related to their lack of gonadal hormones during fetal life (see p. 31).

A special aspect of sex education arises in connection with Turner's syndrome—or any other condition where sterility can be predicted before marriage and adulthood—namely, when and what to say regarding pregnancy and the future. It is generally not wise to avoid the issue on the pretense of sparing the child or teenager, for in fact the only person being spared is oneself. Children overhear much more than they are believed to, especially in medical history-taking and examination-room conferences. They infer sex-related problems from the amount of medical interest in their genitalia. Above all, they see and hear their parents, whose anxiety has them prancing like the metaphorical cat on a hot tin roof every time the subject of childbearing, marriage, or adoption comes up.

It is not necessary to be brutally frank in order to be honest. Any revelation can be made either diplomatically or harshly. I have found that the ideal way to disclose many unpleasant medical predictions is by placing them in the context of probability and the laws of chance. Most people appreciate this degree of scientific humility, because they all know stories of medical predictions that were proven wrong. I disclose the probability of sterility by linking it with the routine story of pregnancy and saying that, on the basis of experience with "cases like yours, doctors expect that you will achieve motherhood by adoption. When the time comes, do not, therefore, keep waiting too long for a pregnancy." For males with corresponding syndromes of infertility there is also the alternative of donor insemination of the wife from the "sperm bank" (see p. 18).

Told in this way, the disclosure has a positive ring. It leaves the ideal of parenthood intact. Only the means is changed. Moreover, it also leaves at least a fragmentary ray of hope that the prediction will prove wrong—and hope is what we all live by to a certain extent.

In very young children it will often be sufficient simply to present the idea of adoption without personalizing it. It is in later childhood and certainly in teenage that the personalized reference is desirable, for then the child may build parenthood by adoption or the sperm bank into the normal rehearsals, fantasies, and expectancies of marriage and future family life. So prepared, the child has an increased chance of success in meeting his or her special role of fatherhood or motherhood —and also of preparing the spouse in advance (see p. 33).

Chapter Four: Gonadal Anomalies

Turner's and Klinefelter's syndromes nicely demonstrate the relationship that may exist between an abnormal number of chromosomes and abnormal gonads with resultant sterility. In other cases of gonadal defect, however, an abnormal chromosome count cannot be implicated, even though there may be an hereditary factor carried in the genes.

When a primitive, undifferentiated gonad develops embryonically into an ovary, the rind or cortical part proliferates. When the core develops, the gonad becomes a testis. With the exception of Turner's syndrome, it is more common to find defective gonadal development in a morphologic male than the female—that is, in the testes more than in the ovaries —which probably has something to do with the fact that nature's embryonal plan in differentiating a male is always to add something to the basic formula—that of the female. The male is the more complex.

Undescended Testes (Cryptorchidism)

The commonest defect in testicular development is the failure of one or both of them to descend. In the majority of instances they will probably descend of their own accord either before or around the time of puberty. It is something of a medical dilemma to decide whether to adopt a hands-off policy, or to try to induce descent by means of hormonal treatment or, as a last resort, by surgery. Any method may fail, since some testes remain undescended because they are imperfect organs to begin with.

In a few, rare instances, an empty scrotum may be a sign of other internal anomalies, such as hermaphroditism (see pp. 43 and 45). It is even possible for a genetic female with two ovaries to be so masculinized externally that the clitoris becomes a normal penis, the labia minora the skin covering the penis, and the labia majora the empty scrotum. Therefore, it is wise for any child with undescended testicles to be given a diagnostic work-up, the younger in age the better, and preferably at a major medical center where the full range of modern diagnostic evaluation is available. Once is enough, however! The first time should be complete. It is too easy for a boy to have so much anxiety and attention focused on his cryptorchidism that he becomes emotionally crippled as well.

Some few boys with testes not in the scrotum will be found to have none at all (Plate 6) or, if they have them, small ones which may even atrophy and disappear (perhaps because of a little-understood condition in which the body becomes immunized against one of its own organs). These boys can be given hormonal replacement therapy, beginning in their early teens, so that they are developmentally indistinguishable from normal. When the testes are missing, they can be replaced with prosthetic substitutes made of silicone rubber (Plate 7). In either case, sexual and married life in adulthood is the same as for men with descended testes of normal size.

There are two precautions to be added in counseling boys with cryptorchidism. One is to be medically frank with them and to keep them abreast of the diagnostic implications, proposed treatment, and prognosis. The other is to make provision for them to be excused from exposing themselves naked in shower and locker rooms if they are too embarrassed by their condition. Only a few will eventually need special counseling on sterility (see pp. 18, 20, and 33).

Because cryptorchidism may require a hospital admission for either diagnostic purposes or surgical treatment, it is one of the many sexual anomalies that produces a problem for the child —and the parents also—in knowing what to tell other people (see p. 51). A bewildered child can be greatly helped by providing him with the appropriate explanatory word or phrase to use—especially with his friends of his own age. Rather than having to circulate information about undescended testes or an artificial testicular implant, he may be better off saying only that he had an exploratory operation, or telling the white lie that his incision was for a hernia repair.

Chapter Five: Fetal Hormonal Anomalies

C ontrary to popular belief, the testes are not dormant throughout life until adolescence. They go through a critical period of activity in fetal life, with profound and lasting effect. If in this critical period of activity differentiation fails, then the internal male (wolffian) organs will remain undeveloped and, subsequently, the external genitals will differentiate as female instead of male. The resultant simulant female will not necessarily have internal female organs (the uterus and fallopian tubes), because the primitive beginnings (the muellerian ducts) of these structures wither away in the male under the influence of a special inhibitor substance. This inhibitor substance works somewhat independently from the masculinizing androgen that encourages growth of the wolffian ducts and the penis and scrotum.

It is possible to produce experimentally these feminizing effects in males by injecting the pregnant mother animal with a hormone, cyproterone (Plates 8A & B). Cyproterone is an antiandrogen which cancels out the normal influence of androgen, the male hormone, from the testes of the fetus. The same effect can be obtained by castrating the fetus at the critical developmental period. It is an incredibly delicate task, if the fetus is to survive and be born—looking like a female!

The opposite effect—experimentally masculinizing a genetic female fetus (with ovaries)—can be achieved by injecting the pregnant mother animal with male sex-hormone (Plate 9). Then the daughter is born with a penis and scrotum. In this experiment, the internal organs are always female. Only the external parts are affected.

Androgen Insensitivity (Testicular Feminizing) Syndrome

The human counterpart of the cyproterone experiment (see above) is the syndrome of androgen insensitivity, formerly known as testicular feminization (Plate 10). Girls or women with this syndrome appear externally no different from normal females except, in some cases, for a swelling or lump in each groin, and perhaps an absence or sparseness of pubic and underarm hair. The cells of the body are totally unable to respond to the male sex hormone, which is made in the testes in normal amounts for a male. They respond instead to the small amount of female sex hormone, estrogen, which is normally made in the testes. The effect of this unusual state of affairs before birth is that masculine internal development commences but does not get completed. It goes far enough, however, to prevent internal female development. Externally, the genitalia differentiate as female, except for a blind vagina (see p. 49), which is usually not deep enough for satisfactory intercourse and needs surgical lengthening in or after late teenage. There is no menstruation and no fertility.

The special needs of sex education for these patients when they are diagnosed—usually in teenage and because of menstrual failure—are counseling with respect to sterility (see p. 20) and an explanation regarding the cause of their condition and any proposed treatment. The source of greatest embarrassment and anxiety is mention of the word "testes." They should only be called sex glands, and an explanation should be given about their paradoxical functioning and lack of germ cells. Each patient needs different degrees of detail. A nurse with the condition, for example, will learn a great many details. In all cases the secret of effective counseling is that the patient is told neither too little nor too much for her own needs, while having complete confidence that the channels of communication always remain open and that she can return at any time for further explanation or more information.

Sterility and, in some cases, the reason for hospitalization for vaginal surgery (see p. 50) are two topics which a girl with testicular feminizing syndrome may have to explain to her boyfriend. What to tell the boyfriend—or girlfriend—is always a matter of great concern to any girl or boy with a history of a sexual deformity or disability. My recommendation is always to say nothing until wedding plans are under very serious consideration. Giving away one's secrets is giving away a part of oneself. They are not to be entrusted casually to a person who may take off with them and spread them around. When wedding plans are being made, a couple are surely in love, unless their relationship is and always will be perfunctory. Being in love is, like grief, an extraordinary episode of human emotion. It deserves far more scientific attention than it has ever been given. The bond that it creates between one person and another is so powerful while it lasts that the lover cannot think of separation from the beloved. Thus, very few weddings are canceled, even as the result of so serious a disclosure as that of reproductive inadequacy. If the marriage should break later, the partner with the disability will have gained so much experience and self-confidence that he will be more easily able to try again under more auspicious circumstances.

No special issue regarding promiscuity arises in the sex education of those who have to learn of their sterility. A person's standards of sexual conduct are much more broadly based than on the fear or possibility of pregnancy. A sterile girl does not take up sexual intercourse simply because she knows of her sterility.

Chapter Six: Internal-Organ Anomalies

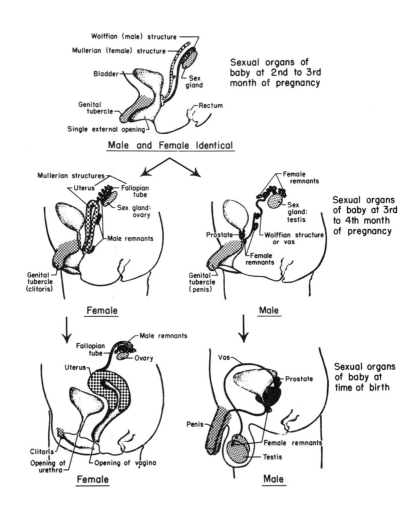

Fig. 3.—Diagrammatic representation of internal sexual differentiation in the fetus.

Early in embryonic development, the wolffian ducts (Fig. 3), from which the internal accessory male organs will develop, lie alongside the muellerian ducts, from which the female internal accessory organs will develop. At this early stage, both sets of ducts are present in male and female. Occasionally, in an otherwise normal male, the muellerian ducts do not become suppressed, as one would expect in a normal male. Consequently, a boy is born with a uterus and fallopian tubes (Plate 11). They are usually found by a surgeon while performing an operation into one side of the scrotum for a hernia caused when these organs were tugged down by a testicle trying to descend unilaterally. Since the condition can be corrected surgically, there are no untoward problems that need to be anticipated in sex education.

There does not appear to be a corresponding condition of persistence of wolffian structures in an otherwise normal female. There are, however, problems of imperfect development of the uterus in a female. Sometimes it may be missing, or it may be misshapen. One such deformity is the bicornate uterus, in which the arms of the fallopian tubes branch off too soon, like the arms of a Y instead of a T. Fertility may or may not be affected. Otherwise there are no special problems for sex education.

Chapter Seven: External-Organ Anomalies

Embryologically, the external organs are the last of the sexual morphology to be completed. Here nature's plan is to take the same initial structures, making of them components of either the male or female genitalia. The genital tubercle grows out to become the penis or retracts to become the clitoris. The skin which wraps around the penis and fuses along the raphe of the underside to form the urethral canal has its homologue in the hood of the clitoris extending lengthways as the labia minora. The skin of the scrotum, which also fuses on the midline, is the homologue of the labia majora which remain unfused to reveal the genital openings.

It is relatively simple, in such a plan of biological engineering, for the external genitals to be left unfinished (Fig. 4), neither fully masculinized nor feminized. The unfinished state of either sex looks remarkably like that of the other. There is a genital tubercle which could be either a large clitoris or a small penis. This organ has an open gutter underneath it instead of a covered urethral tube. The urinary orifice is at its root or base, more or less in the female position. The opening at the base may be small and lead directly to the bladder; or it may be a quite large urogenital sinus from the interior of which can be traced both the urethral and vaginal passages. The latter may either connect with the cervix of the uterus or end blindly. Outside and below the opening, it will be ambiguous whether there is a scrotum with incomplete fusion or labia majora more fused than they should have been.

Unfinished external sexual differentiation leaves one thoroughly confused as to the sex of a baby. From external

41

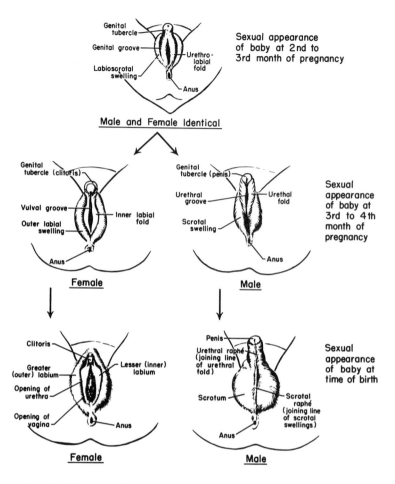

Fig. 4.—Diagrammatic representation of external sexual differentiation in the fetus.

appearance alone, such a baby could be a male hermaphrodite, a female hermaphrodite or a so called true hermaphrodite. By definition, a male hermaphrodite has two testicles, though sometimes one may be missing, and a female hermaphrodite two ovaries. Both types are also sometimes called pseudohermaphrodites. A true hermaphrodite, by definition, has some ovarian and some testicular tissue either separate or mixed together in the same gonad. All three forms of hermaphroditism are equally genuine.

42

It is not imperative to have ambiguous-looking sex organs to be classified as an hermaphrodite. The ambiguity may exist internally, as in the androgen insensitivity (testicular feminizing) syndrome or in the male with a normal penis and a uterus. However, the classical dilemma in hermaphroditism is that of ambiguity of external appearance.

Female Hermaphroditism

This type of ambiguity is produced in genetic females by the presence of too much masculinizing hormone at a critical period of fetal development. This masculinizing hormone is produced in the adrenogenital syndrome by overactive, erroneously working adrenal glands (Plates 12 and 13). In this condition, the adrenal cortex makes the wrong hormone—androgen instead of cortisone. The basic cause is a recessive genetic trait. It is the commonest cause of female hermaphroditism and can be controlled by cortisone-replacement treatment (Plate 14).

The other type of female hermaphroditism is produced by abnormal amounts of androgen from the mother. The mother may have had an androgen-producing tumor while pregnant. The greatest likelihood, however, is that she had a prescription for progestin (pregnancy hormone) to prevent a threatened miscarriage. In a few instances of this treatment, the body utilizes the progestin as if it were androgen, so that a female fetus occasionally becomes masculinized (Plate 15). The metabolism of one hormone into another within the human body is not surprising, since biochemically the sex hormones are all "first cousins."

In today's medicine, the treatment for female hermaphroditism—surgical and hormonal—is effective. The most important thing is early diagnosis, ideally at the time of birth. Then the girl can grow up oblivious of ever having had a problem. Her need for special sex education is then correspondingly minimized.

Male Hermaphroditism

The same ambiguities of the external organs occur in male hermaphroditism when there is a developmental failure of the male-hormonal effect. The failure may be either in the production of male hormone or in its utilization. The primary cause for either failure still remains to be discovered. In some cases of familial occurrence there is no doubt that a genetic factor is involved.

Complete failure of fetal masculinization results in a baby who is a morphologic female as in the androgen insensitivity (testicular feminizing) syndrome (see p. 32). There are all degrees of failure of masculinization between this extreme on the one hand, and the normal male, on the other. The closer the resemblance of the external organs to the normal female, the less is the likelihood that anything can ever be done to permit a normal male sexual life (Plate 16). Therefore there are many male hermaphrodites who should be designated female at birth, with a program then, and again in teenage, of appropriate surgical correction and hormonal treatment. So treated, and with the parents properly counseled (see p. 61), such individuals grow up and function very well as girls. They differentiate a feminine psychosexual identity. There are no special difficulties subsequently in their sex education over and above those of other individuals with chromosomal anomalies, sterility, and contradictory sexual structures. All of these issues can be diplomatically handled, with a good outcome, as in the manner described in connection with Turner's syndrome and the androgen insensitivity (testicular feminizing) syndrome (see pp. 18, 20, and 33).

A specially trying situation arises when a male hermaphrodite with a phallus large enough to justify his assignment and surgical correction as a boy reaches his teens and proves to have the syndrome of feminizing testes (Plate 17). He develops breasts and totally lacks the masculine body traits. Since his body is resistant to the male sex hormone, treatment with it is useless. His voice remains high-pitched, his face unbearded, and his body feminine rather than masculine in contour. The erectile mechanism of his penis may fail. The prostate gland may not be stimulated to produce ejaculatory fluid. Pleasant erotic feeling is not missing, but it does not reach the true climactic peak of orgasm. Perhaps his greatest mortification is that he does not achieve a proper adult male appearance of aging and is constantly mistaken for much younger than his chronological age. The disparity may be so great that at thirty-two a man is always responded to by strangers as sixteen or seventeen—which was particularly galling to one man who had established a companionate marriage and was mistaken everywhere for his wife's son. In his case, he did not have even the appearance of aging as a female, as his feminizing testes had been removed earlier. His body was totally un-responsive to male hormone injections.

It is possible to forestall such an unhappy ending by using in early infancy a trial test of androgen ointment on the penis. If the penis enlarges and pubic hair growth begins, one has evidence of the body's ability to respond to the male sex hormone. Without this evidence, it is preferable to set a pro-gram of surgical feminization and raise the baby as a girl.

In teenage and adulthood, any help that can be given in sex education and counseling is at best supportive, since the basic dilemmas cannot be resolved. Nonetheless, it is amazing how well some of these patients do maintain their self-confidence and rise above the adversity of their lives.

True Hermaphroditism

From the point of view of sex education, nothing new is encountered in true hermaphroditism (Plate 18) that may not also be encountered in either male or female hermaphro-ditism. There may be some explaining to do, regarding a chromosomal contradiction, if the rearing so requires. True hermaphrodites typically have a 44 + XX chromosome count, irrespective of the presence of testes and the amount of masculine anatomy. For a true hermaphrodite raised and living as a boy and feeling like one, there is thus a chromosomal contradiction analogous to that in the girl with testicular feminization. Likewise, there arises a rather delicate counseling situation if a true hermaphrodite living as a boy develops breasts at puberty and begins to menstruate as a result of the estrogenic activity of hitherto unsuspected ovaries. The same has been known to occur in the case of female hermaphro-dites incompletely diagnosed at birth and assigned to be raised as boys. The reverse also occurs when true or male her-maphrodites, assigned and living as girls, develop hormonal masculinization at puberty.

In such cases, and in any others of hermaphroditism where contradictions and incongruities occur, the best procedure of sex education and counseling is one of not creating emotional indigestion by saying too much, too soon, and also of not allowing emotional malnutrition by saying too little, too late.

45

Explanation can be based on the premise of the child's having been born sexually unfinished—an extraordinarily useful term that has saved many hundreds of patients and their parents the mortification of terms like "freak," "morphodite," "half-boy" and "half-girl," "neuter sex," and so on.

The concept of being sexually unfinished lends itself nicely to use of the diagrams of embryonic differentiation (See Figs. 3 and 4, pp. 38 and 42). From these diagrams it is possible to give a rational explanation of how elements of the reproductive system of one sex can be found contradictorily developed (or not vestigiated) in the presence of organs of the other sex. In this way nature's error can be accounted for. The patient and/or parent is able to comprehend the rationale of treatment and to feel the reassurance and conviction of correctness that comes from participating in and understanding the meaning of a decision.

In most such cases of adolescent incongruity, the patient's feeling and conviction of sexual identity will be in accord with the sex of rearing, and the surgical and hormonal corrections will be made accordingly. However, one dare not take for granted that such will be the case. The chief reason for medical frankness is that it does allow the patient to state his or her own case and weigh the possibility of a sex reassignment (see p. 86).

Hypospadias

The type of unfinished penis, already several times referred to, with an unfused open gutter instead of a closed urethral tube on its under side, and the urinary orifice at its base instead of at its tip, represents the most extreme degree of hypospadias (Plate 19). At the other end of the scale is the mild degree of hypospadias in which the urinary orifice is only one or two millimeters displaced from its proper position. Mild hypospadias does not hinder effective urination or copulation and so does not need surgical intervention as do the more severe degrees. Other things being equal, it is desirable for a boy to begin school with the severe abnormality corrected. For the best surgical result, however, it may not be advisable to complete the surgical repair so early. In this circumstance, sexual counseling is imperative so that the boy has a sense of the predictability of things to come. He needs also special provisions for privacy in urination—for example, being shown the location of school latrines before the first day of school and being given permission to use them unaccompanied by a crowd of other boys. Later, he may want to be exempted from undressing in the school shower or locker room.

At all ages, children need to know in advance what is planned surgically when they go to the operating room. Mystified by the unknown, a child can easily conjecture that he will emerge from the operation minus the penis that he treasures and hopes will one day be a good one. When admitted for hypospadiac repair, the older boy needs an explanation of his hospitalization to give to his school friends and casual acquaintances. He is best advised to give a simplified statement such as "urinary blockage" or "problem of infection."

Hypospadias may or may not be accompanied by undescended testes (see p. 25). If so, they may descend of their own accord or under the influence of hormonal treatment with gonadotropin. In some cases they will remain undescended or missing, in which case artificial testes can be put in place (see p. 26).

Except in cases of an excessively small organ to begin with, hypospadiac repair, even in the severe cases, typically results in a functional penis adequate for normal sexual function in adulthood. Should sterility be predicted, special counseling is needed (see pp. 18, 20, and 33).

Penile Agenesis

Not far removed from hermaphroditism, in terms of its practical management, is the condition of a boy born with agenesis of the penis also known as microphallus (Plate 20). Typically in this condition, the penis is a tiny organ, no more than 2 cm. long. It is for the most part a skinny tube with no body to it except for a small glans at the tip. Usually, the testes are small and defective. The cause of the condition is not known.

It is true that penises come in all sizes, as do hands and feet, and may bear very little relationship to the size of the rest of the body. Though size may be a matter of vanity, a great deal of variance is allowable before a penis is too big to permit satisfactory coitus or too small to do so. Generalized obesity is more likely to be a coital handicap, by hiding the penis under a roll of fat, than is the smallness of the penis. In the case of the microphallus, however, the organ is definitely too small to permit satisfactory copulation. It is, therefore, fairly common to recommend to the parents that they raise such a baby as a girl. This is, of course, a very difficult decision for them to make, and they must be given all the information needed to understand the rationale of the decision. First and foremost, they need to know that gender identity and role are not preordained by genetic and intrauterine events alone, but that psychosexual differentiation is largely a postnatal process and highly responsive to social stimulation and experience. Thus, they can expect their baby to grow up normally as a girl. Surgical correction in the newborn period will give the child the visible appearance of a girl, and a second-stage correction in teenage or young adulthood will produce an artificial vagina adequate for intercourse. Hormonal replacement treatment in the early teens will produce the physique and appearance of a female. Fertility is not seriously an issue, since the possibility that the testes would have been fertile had they been left in place is open to doubt. In some cases they may even have been feminizing testes.

In such cases of the reversal of sex by assignment, it is of crucial importance that the parents achieve a feeling of conviction in what they do. Then they will be able to rear the child consistently as a girl. If they are in doubt, then their ambivalence will almost certainly communicate itself to the child. To some degree, the conviction will express itself in their equanimity in answering whatever questions the child may ask and in breaking the ice to give whatever information they may need to give. Their simplest security device is to refer emotion-laden issues to the doctor or the professional medical sex educator. They themselves can rely very much on the explanatory formula, already mentioned, of the child's having been born sexually unfinished.

Not all cases of penile agenesis have been given, nor will be given, the above-recommended treatment. In some cases one will be confronted with the problem of giving sex education to a boy without a penis. He will be particularly in need of an outsider to whom he can reveal in confidence even such secret

48

thoughts as that perhaps he should change and be a girl. The conjectures and ruminations of childhood go much deeper than we surface-reading adults sometimes care to have to face!

It has proved possible in some cases to ameliorate the obloquy of childhood by giving the boy with a microphallus a prescription of testosterone ointment to apply locally to the penis. The male sex hormone in the ointment produces what is actually a localized puberty. The penis grows and pubic hair appears. The boost in morale is great. It outweighs the unfortunate fact that the treatment has done nothing more than accelerate the growth of the penis to its adult size, and that it will not become greatly larger when the rest of the body enters puberty, when testosterone will be needed again orally or by injection. However, the increase in morale may have enabled the boy to join in sports and gym, appearing naked before his age-mates.

As he approaches his teens, he can learn in more detail about his prospects for sexual intercourse in adulthood—about nongenital techniques of erotic stimulation and about the use of an artificial or prosthetic penis for the greater stimulation of his partner in simulated coitus. By knowing in advance that the future is not entirely black, he will be better prepared to go through the normal phases of adolescent social and romantic development. Eventually he will be able to find someone to marry—someone whose love and need for him are as great as his for her. Somewhere there is a lover for everyone, handicap and all, who has the confidence to find her.

Vaginal Atresia

As a life dilemma, the female deformity corresponding to agenesis of the penis is absence or closure of the vagina (Plate 21). The same condition commonly exists in girls with the androgen insensitivity (testicular feminizing) syndrome. In some cases the vaginal opening may be present, but with insufficient depth to the vaginal cavity beyond. If the ovaries are present and the uterus is well enough formed to produce menstruation, then there may be a problem of menstrual pain, owing to the retention of menstrual blood unable to escape from the sealed-off uterus. Alternatively, there may be no menstruation at all, if the uterus itself, as well as the vagina, is also missing or incompletely formed. In either case, it is surgically possible to construct a vaginal passage, lined with a skin graft taken from the thigh, that will permit a normal coital life in marriage. The special issues in sex education for a girl so affected include sterility (see p. 20) and what and when to tell her boyfriend (see p. 33). They also include the decision of when to be admitted to the hospital for the surgical correction.

The surgical procedure is an elective one, so the girl should be allowed freedom in choosing the time of her operation. The age considerations are, on one hand, surgical—that the body should be fully grown before the vagina is constructed —and, on the other hand, psychological—but the girl should not be unnecessarily embarrassed in her romantic life by having to confess to her future husband that she will need surgery before being able to have sexual intercourse.

In times past there was a tendency to advise corrective surgery "when you are married." The logic implicit in this advice is that a surgically constructed vagina needs to be kept open by the wearing of a form which may not be as necessary if the vagina is regularly used by a penis in sexual intercourse. Marriage, however, should not be made to appear as a necessary prerequisite for surgery, and a girl should not be made to feel that she may be considered a whore by asking for her vagina to be constructed before she has begun to think of marriage. For many sensitive souls, it is scarcely possible to have the courage to think of going steady, getting engaged, and marrying until the embarrassment of the sexual deformity has been resolved.

The decision regarding the timing of corrective vaginal surgery almost invariably involves the family. Psychologic counseling here can be invaluable, since the emotional needs of the parents may not coincide in urgency with those of the patient. It may be very important to a teenaged girl, for example, not to have a skin-graft scar exposed on her thigh during the summer swimming season, since it will require an explanation to her friends and acquaintances which she is ill-equipped to give. Or, she may not be able to cope with the wearing of a vaginal form while wishing to keep up her interests in sports and athletics at high school or college. One girl may be able to enter the hospital for a vaginal reconstruction, explaining the purpose of the operation to her future husband and being visited by him daily. Another girl may become emotionally overwrought because she does not know how to answer anyone who, having discovered the secret of her hospital admission, wants to know what was wrong with her. Her emotional dilemma becomes exacerbated if she and her parents are unable to agree on what replies they will give to their curious friends and acquaintances.

I have found that it is best for a patient not to confabulate or tell lies, since it is too difficult to be consistent in untruth over a period of time. Each patient has to work out a formula to suit her special circumstances, dependent on what people have been told ahead of time. Usually, there are a few very close relatives or friends who need to be told as much as the patient herself knows. Next comes a circle of friends who feel they have the right to be curious and will not be satisfied with a brush-off. These people may be given vague and general explanations such as "hymen trouble," "menstrual blockage," or "misplacement of the internal organs." Such explanations are not false, while at the same time they are not too personally revealing. They also permit the patient to evade further questioning by saying that she prefers to avoid talking about herself, or that she is not medically expert enough to answer more questions. Beyond the circle of friends lies the world of more casual acquaintances and work-mates. These people need very little explanation at all—perhaps just the simple statement, "I don't care to talk about it."

It has, in my experience, proved to be of great importance to girls with vaginal atresia to rehearse ahead of time what they will say about themselves to the different people who push them for an explanation. It is equally important that the girl and her parents agree on a formula so that they do not tell inconsistent stories.

Phimosis

Phimosis is a tightness of the foreskin that prevents it from being drawn back over the glans of the penis (Plate 22). If it is forced back, the foreskin painfully constricts the neck of the penis as if it were a tight rubber band. If in coitus the glans penis stays covered by the foreskin which does not retract, there is no pain. The major inconvenience of phimosis for most individuals is hygienic. Circumcision may or may not be recommended. Prior to an admission for circumcision, a boy or man needs some explanatory counseling with respect to the procedure itself and what to expect regarding sexual function.

Circumcision does not seriously alter the sensitivity of the penis and its arousal to orgasm, though there have been no pre- and postoperative studies of men circumcised in adulthood to document whether there might be any changes at all. From the study of patients who have suffered severe mutilating injury or loss of the penis, or who have undergone surgical penectomy for cancer, for the correction of hermaphroditism, or for feminine reassignment in the case of transexualism, it is evident that astonishingly large amounts of genital tissue may be removed without destruction of the capacity to reach orgasm.

The practice of circumcising male babies born with a perfectly normal penis is usually a safe procedure, but errors do occur in which some of the body of the penis is removed along with the foreskin. With considerable frequency, far too much of the skin-covering of the penis is removed, so that what remains is stretched too tight during erection. Many circumcisions would be cosmetically much neater had they been done by a plastic surgeon.

The origin of the custom of circumcision is lost in prehistory, as is also the custom of the Australian aboriginals of subincising the urethra, slitting it open from the tip of the penis to the base, to create an artificial hypospadias with the urinary opening in a feminine position. Both customs could have their origins in blood sacrifice and could be an attenuated form of human sacrifice and a symbolic substitute for it. In some ethnic societies, notably in East Africa and South Arabia, the hood of the clitoris and the labia minora may be removed in an act of ritual circumcision of females. Ritual circumcision of males has a wide ethnographic range, being known from Australia to the Middle East. It is an obligatory religious ritual for Jews and Moslems. In recent times it has become a fashion in non-Jewish America and elsewhere, especially where babies are born in hospitals. It is done ostensibly for hygienic reasons, but far more likely is simply an example of what, in anthropological terminology, is cultural borrowing. The custom has become grafted to the fashionable rather than the ceremonial part of the borrower's culture. Its continued viability is emotional and rationalized rather than intelligent and rational. Many believe the custom could well be discontinued.

Other External Anomalies

From the point of view of sex education, the various counseling issues that arise in consequence of anomalies of the external organs have all been covered under the syndromes already presented. The same principles can be applied to the other deformities that may occur, like epispadias (Plate 23), which involve not only the reproductive organs, but also the urinary and/or defecatory systems in addition. Epispadias is a severe condition in which the bladder empties directly through a gaping orifice in the lower abdominal wall, the penis itself, or the clitoris in the female, appearing to be split on its dorsal (upward) side. Surgical repair is possible, but urinary continence may be a problem. In the male, the repaired penis may be too small for adequate coitus, may not be quite correctly situated, and may not erect well. In the most severe male cases, with a very small, very deformed penis, it may be advisable at birth to declare the child as a female, and to undertake feminizing surgical repair, as is done in penile agenesis. The more usual procedure, and the one always to be followed when the penis is big enough, is to repair the male as a male.

Chapter Eight: Hypothalamic Anomalies of Sex

The pituitary gland sits in the middle of the cranium at a point approximately behind the bridge of the nose. It is, among other things, a regulator gland. One of its functions is to regulate the hormone production of the gonads or sex glands (ovaries or testes). The pituitary not only is situated anatomically in close proximity to the hypothalamus, but also is closely linked functionally to this small part of the brain, which is amazingly diverse in its influence on the essential vital processes of survival and reproduction.

One of the newest advances in sex research has been the discovery that in males, at the time in fetal development when the fetal testes are hormonally responsible for organizing the differentiation of male instead of female anatomy (see Figs. 3 and 4, pp. 38 and 42), their hormone is also responsible for organizing the masculinity of certain nuclei in the hypothalamus. In the lower mammals, these are nuclei that prevent the cyclic function of the pituitary in males. In females, cyclic pituitary function is not prevented, so periodic estrus occurs. Nearby hypothalamic nuclei regulate mating behavior in synchrony with the estrus cycle in the female and, in the male, in response to the stimulus of estrus in the female.

It is still too early in the progress of research to say what are, or what might be, the anomalies of hypothalamic sexual differentiation in man. It is possible that a relationship may be uncovered between some of the psychosexual disorders in man and the anomalies of hypothalamic function. It is possible, for example, that the fetal masculinizing effect on the hypothalamus may not have taken place at the critical time in development, in certain individuals, or that the neural cells of the hypothalamus were unable to respond to it on schedule.

The hypothalamus also has another sexual role not specifically related to sex differences, but connected with the timing of puberty. It is quite likely that in the hypothalamus is a part of the brain mechanism that carries the biological clock of puberty, probably in association with the temporal lobe of the cerebral cortex. A tumor or other lesion of the hypothalamus may set the clock of puberty going too soon and is one cause of precocious puberty, especially in males (see p. 67).

Chapter Nine: Anomalies of Assignment and Rearing

The sex of assignment is the product of both an official act in the signing of the birth certificate and a reiterative routine in all the daily acts of rearing that decrees and confirms masculine or feminine expectancies. The rearing of an anatomically normal child in contradiction to the correct assignment is almost never heard of. When it does occur, one or both parents can be considered psychotic. Perfectly normal parents, by contrast, can become the unsuspecting characters in a drama of anomalous assignment when a child is born with abnormal sex organs.

Some of these wrong assignments will be, in effect, simply wrong announcements, for the initial error will be discovered when the diagnosis is completely decided within a few days of birth or, at most, a few weeks. Then the problem to be faced is simply a reannouncement of sex. It is one that does not involve the baby at so young an age, as it would do were he old enough to have developed a self-awareness as a boy or girl. The people for whom this neonatal sex-reannouncement is a problem are the parents, older siblings, other close relatives, friends, and the community. It is not as difficult a problem as one might think.

In some older medical writings, it used to be commented in passing that when a new announcement of sex was necessary, the parents should move to a new town, find a new job, sever all connections with the past, and start life anew. I have found that this formula is completely untenable. People who have followed it live haunted lives, pursued by the ghosts of their past and constantly intimidated by them. There is always the nagging, realistic fear that somehow the secret will out, for it is impossible to guarantee total obliteration of one's past.

The alternative is to deal with the reannouncement openly. The first step is to make sure that the parents have the necessary medical knowledge (albeit somewhat simplified) to be able to explain their dilemma to themselves prior to explaining it to other people. This same knowledge will help them to feel convinced that what is being done is correct and is their own decision as well as that of the doctor. Otherwise, they might easily feel that they are acquiescing to a program that is trial-and-error—and that could prove all error. Once again, the concept of being sexually unfinished is invaluable, as are the diagrams that illustrate it (see Figs. 3 and 4, pp. 38 and 42). Many parents find it very helpful to take a reprint of these diagrams to use when they talk with their relatives and others. They also are helped by being given a brief medical vocabulary with which to identify their child's anomalous condition —terms like "hypospadias," "enlarged clitoris," "overactive adrenal glands," "incomplete labial fusion," "hormonal insufficiency," and so on. I usually write these terms as an aid to their memory. There is a magic about words and a power in technical terms that silences idle curiosity, for the idly curious hate to have their ignorance exposed. Medical terminology also enables a parent (or an older patient) to have the last word in any silly conversation, by telling the inquisitive one, if necessary, to satisfy his curiosity by speaking with a doctor.

The first people with whom the parents need to deal are their closest relatives, usually their parents. Then they will usually explain their predicament to a few very close friends. I recommend that they deliberately choose a more or less public figure who is connected with the family—like the pastor, the family doctor, a nurse, a schoolteacher, or lawyer— and give this person the facts of the situation. They should ask him to tell the truth to other curious members of the community and at the same time request them to stop any further gossip for the sake of the child's future. Some mothers have found that it is immensely helpful to show their baby, once the surgical correction has been accomplished, to a few key people, such as the baby-sitting mothers who take turns caring for infants during church gatherings.

Those who are most likely to be overlooked at the time of a sex reannouncement are the older brothers and sisters. They, of all people, deserve an accurate explanation of the baby's having been born unfinished. Otherwise, they would logically be entitled to reach the conclusion that the same thing could happen to them, with or against their will. Parents are often too embarrassed or squeamish to talk straightforwardly with their older children, offering instead some platitudes about God's intentions or something similar. Therefore, the professional outsider has a duty to arrange, if possible, to talk to these older siblings himself.

It will undoubtedly also be necessary for him, as the years pass, to talk directly to the patient, now grown older. He will be able to maintain an outsider's impartiality, whereas the parents will perhaps be emotional and disconcerted. As in other embarrassing sex-education situations, they can refer their child's difficult inquiries to the professional who, in turn, can thaw the channels of communication between them by conducting a final joint session in which shared knowledge is made explicit.

Direct talk with the child is an absolute imperative when the possibility of changing the sex of rearing is raised, not in the neonatal period, but many years later after postnatal psychosexual differentiation is already so far advanced that it is irreversible. In this case the issue is not the simple one of sex reannouncement, but the far more complex one of sex reassignment (see p. 85ff).

Chapter Ten: Pubertal Hormonal Anomalies

In girls, the onset of puberty is expected from age 11½ through 14½, and in boys, from 12½ through 15½, more or less. Nature does not always play the game as expected, however. It is possible for puberty to begin as early as in the first year of life, or to be delayed until the late teens or beyond.

Precocious Puberty

When a girl shows the first signs of sexual development, at age ten, or even nine, the onset of her puberty, though early, is generally considered to be within normal limits. The same is true of a boy whose puberty has its onset at age eleven. Before these ages, the onset of puberty is considered precocious (Plate 24). Early puberty, in many cases, can be explained as the result of a premature signal from the hypothalamic-pituitary alarm clock, without any other pathology (Plate 25). In other cases, the early sounding of the pubertal alarm clock is the secondary result of a tumor or other pathology in the hypothalamic-pituitary structures. The tumor or other lesion is not necessarily dangerous or fatal. Boys are more likely than girls to show brain involvement as a cause of precocious puberty. Boys are also less likely than girls to develop precocious puberty. In other words, girls are more likely than boys to begin an early pubertal development, especially at age nine, without any brain complications for the diagnostician to be worried about. For either sex, however, the first requirement when puberty begins early is a complete diagnostic evaluation to rule out the possibility of dangerous complications, especially a brain tumor, and to establish the benign diagnosis of idiopathic sexual precocity. In boys, it will be necessary to rule out the diagnosis of precocious hyper-adrenocortical virilism—that is, the male adrenogenital syn-drome (Plate 26)—in which early development is not accom-panied by testicular maturation, but is caused by excess androgens from the adrenal gland.

There is no completely effective way at the present time of delaying early puberty, except of the adrenogenital variety in males—and then only if they are treated with cortisone from infancy onward. Older boys with the same syndrome, who are well virilized before cortisone treatment is begun, pass directly into normal early puberty under the influence of testicular hormones. Conversely, the analogous condition occurs, with the production of feminizing ovarian hormones, in the virilized female adrenogenital hermaphrodite first treated with cortisone after infancy (see page 43).

The new antiandrogen, cyproterone (see p. 31), may prove useful for blocking idiopathic precocity in boys. Until it is released for general use, the best treatment is the use of progestinic drug, Provera (medroxyprogesterone acetate), which has a male sex-hormone suppressing effect. This same drug is also used for girls with precocious puberty. It retards breast development and prevents the onset of menstruation, but it does not hold back statural growth and may have an adverse effect on menstrual regularity when the girl is older and no longer needs the drug.

Even with the help of drugs to slow down premature de-velopment, the management of precocious puberty relies heavily on psychologic medicine in counseling and sex educa-tion. The principle on which counseling is founded is that of reducing the disparities between chronological age, statural or physique age, and social age. Social age (including intellec-tual age and academic age), if left to its own devices, tends to develop parallel to chronological age, and to be divorced from physique age. Because the physical size and energy of a physically precocious child permits his mixing with older and bigger children, social age may become advanced over chron-ological age. In fact, social age can and should be deliberately accelerated by academic advancement, when the IQ permits, and by social and recreational mixing with children a year or two older. In this way, the ideal is achieved of reducing the number of years in which the child exists in a no-man's land of disparity between physique and social development.

Sex education is a must for all children, as far as I am concerned, and is certainly a must for those with early puberty. Left to themselves to play, infants and children tend to rehearse in play, as do macaque monkeys and other primates, the component acts of the total mating response. In monkeys, total deprivation of play, including sexual play, results in severe aberration of mating behavior in adolescence and adulthood, usually with total failure to breed successfully. Should pregnancy be achieved, then mothering is grossly defective, so much so that the infant monkey perishes.

One can scarcely envisage, in the near future, the social acceptance of copulation games in kindergarten. Therefore, adults must substitute with words the sex education lessons with which children would spontaneously experiment for themselves, were they not exposed to the restraints and taboos of convention. Deeds must be replaced with words, if children are to have the necessary truth about the role of their bodies in the reproduction of their kind, as well as the necessary sense and freedom of gender identity to be able, in adulthood, to put this truth into practice.

The sex education story which I formulated some years ago, I tell along with illustrative diagrams (Figs. 5–11). It is a story told step by step. The amount unfolded at any one time depends on the age and interest of the child and the frequency with which one sees him. Parents are in an ideal position to gauge how much to tell, for they are constantly available for an added installment. The tale begins with the baby egg, without a shell and no bigger than the dot made by the point of a pencil. This baby egg is released from the ovary into the baby nest. The egg grows, the limbs bud, and the organs form, until the baby is ready to be born. It gets out head first—so that the shoulders can be tucked close to the body—down the baby tunnel or canal. The egg is able to start growing into a baby only when it is joined by a sperm, which is made by the father. There are three hundred million sperms, and they have a swimming race, wiggling their long propelling tails, to see which one can reach the egg first. There is only one winner! The prize is to make the egg grow into a baby. The winner burrows its head into the soft wall of the egg and

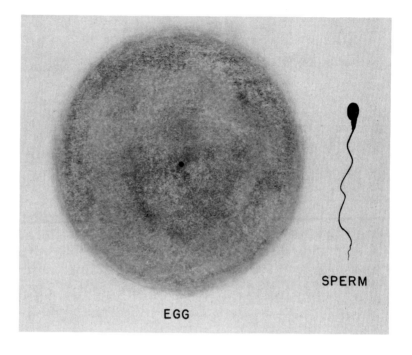

SPERM

EGG

Fig. 5.—A real baby egg is no bigger than a dot made with the point of
a pencil in the middle of this drawing. A real sperm is so
small that it cannot be seen without a microscope.

70

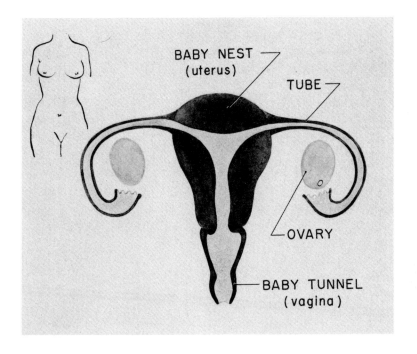

Fig. 6.—The female internal organs for producing a baby.

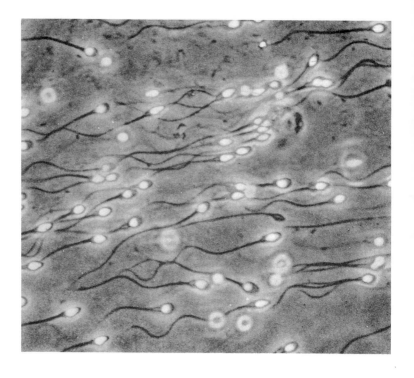

Fig. 7.—The swimming race of the sperms. There are three hundred million of them—but only one winner!

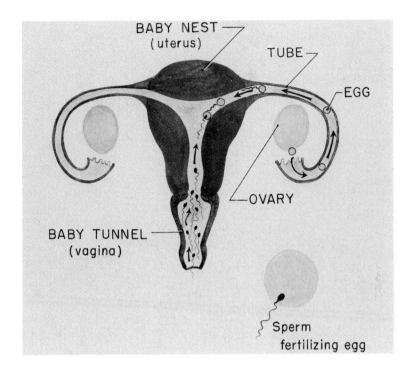

Fig. 8.—Sperms swim up to look for an egg, and an egg moves along the tube looking for a sperm. The winning sperm fertilizes the egg.

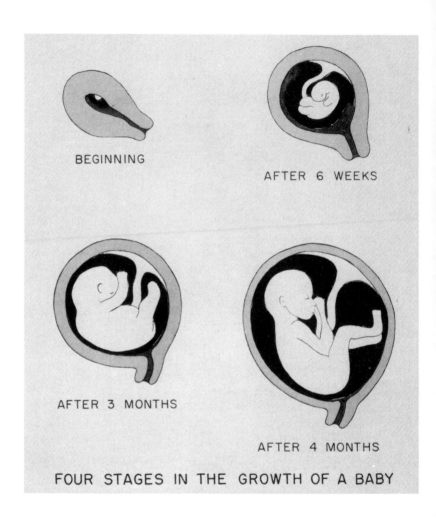

BEGINNING

AFTER 6 WEEKS

AFTER 3 MONTHS

AFTER 4 MONTHS

FOUR STAGES IN THE GROWTH OF A BABY

Fig. 9.—A baby begins like a small spot on the wall of the baby nest. It is connected to the wall with the cord that brings nourishment from the mother through the baby's navel or belly button.

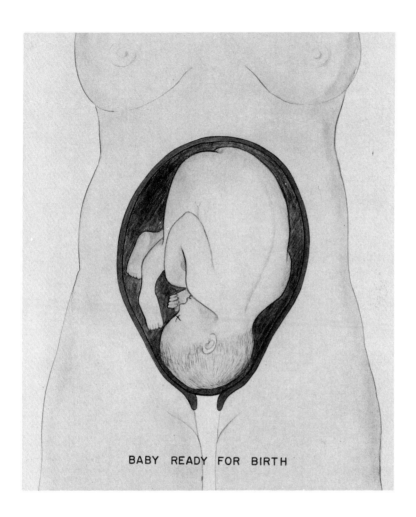

BABY READY FOR BIRTH

Fig. 10.—After nine months the baby is born. It comes out head first with its arms tucked at its sides. Feet first and arms spread, it would get stuck.

75

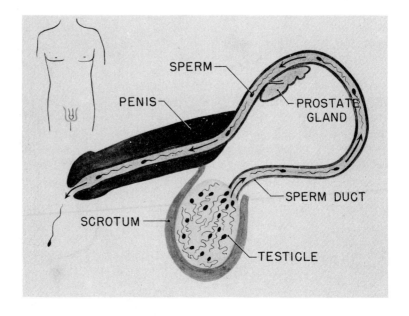

Fig. 11.—Sperms are made in the testicle. They swim and keep alive in the fluid made in the prostate gland. They are pumped out through the penis, which swells up with blood until it is solid enough to fit the vagina. In this way, none of the sperms will be lost.

76

drops off its tail. Then the egg fixes itself onto the wall of the baby nest, where it can share the mother's blood, in which food and air are "dissolved," and grow from a blob into a real person.

Sperms are made in the father's testicles, which are really sperm factories. They have to swim away from the testicles, through a long tube inside the body, and out through the penis. The penis stands up stiff and straight so that it can fit into the baby tunnel, where the sperms and their swimming juice are pumped out. That gives them a good start on their swimming race. It makes sure that they have a fair chance of finding the egg far away inside the baby nest. Sperms are so small that a pencil point is too big to draw one. The drawing is a super-giant-sized, instead of a real, life-sized, sperm. You can see a real sperm only if you have a microscope to magnify it.

I tell this story to parents not only so that they too can tell it to their children, in installments for the very young, but also so they can repeat it for those who might forget. Moreover, it solves the problem of terminology (the medical terms are added later), which has for many parents proved the biggest single stumbling block to effective communication with young children on matters of reproduction. With this stumbling block removed early in life, child and parent can keep in mutual contact on matters of sexual behavior and on what may be called the psychology and sociology of sex as contrasted with the physiology of sex. During early childhood, education in the sociology of sex means, among other things, advice on where and when to talk about the physiology of sex. The recommendation of keeping it a family and medical secret reserved for "your Mommy, your Daddy, and your doctor" is a simple expedient that prevents social embarrassment for parents at the dinner table, in the neighborhood, and elsewhere. Adolescence is the age during which the sociology and psychology of sex and falling in love are preeminent in sex education. It is, therefore, in the sex education of adolescence that parents reap the greatest reward for having kept open the channels of mutual confidence by early frankness.

In cases where freedom of communication breaks down, the responsibility lies with adults to thaw the frost of silence. It is not enough to follow the maxim, "Answer your children's questions truthfully when they ask them," because the child who has frozen up will avoid asking any at all. One way to break the deadlock is to use the technique of the parable—to tell a story of a child in a similar predicament, who finally developed enough confidence to tell and ask about thus and so. The parable technique guarantees a child that he is not unique, and, above all, it guarantees that the adult's ears can listen to sex talk without exploding.

I am very frank when I talk with pubertally precocious children, because I want them to know at least one person to whom they can bring any topic of their sexual experience or curiosity, when they need to or feel ready to. Normal adolescents have their own age-mates from whom they learn and find reassurance about teenage sex, but the precocious developer has no pubertal contemporaries to guide—or misguide—him regarding romantic feelings, dating, involvement with older teenagers, parental discipline, masturbation, and so on. Children with precocious puberty respond very well to counseling and guidance. They display the same range of balance and common sense as do most adolescents during normal puberty. Finally, their contemporaries catch up with them, and they become lost to view except that, especially in the case of the boys, they are short-statured in adulthood. (In early life their bones grew and matured so rapidly that there was not time for them to grow long.)

Pubertal Delay or Failure

At the opposite end of the spectrum from precocious puberty is delayed puberty (Plate 27). The child who lags in reaching puberty at the normal age may be showing the first signs of what will actually be chronic failure to commence puberty spontaneously, as in several of the syndromes already mentioned. It will clearly be important to establish the diagnosis and to distinguish special conditions of defect or impairment from the uncomplicated type of delay that may be simply a sign of "late blooming." Although it is a good general principle not to interfere when nature will do the work unaided, there are limits on how long to wait for nature. In the case of late blooming, when puberty is prolonged far beyond the early teens, the deleterious effect of physical infantilism on social and psychologic maturation is ordinarily too great a risk to justify prolonged postponement of hormonal "starter" treatment. The treatment may be to prime the gonads into action with sex hormones or to imitate the triggering action of the pituitary on the gonads with gonadotropin. In either case, the treatment should be conservative, for fear of injuring fertility. It is impossible to know how extensive the fertility risk is, especially in males, since many cases that may seem to be simply late blooming will actually be more complex cases, destined to infertility even without any treatment to induce pubertal onset.

Chronic pubertal failure is more common in males than in females. It is sometimes primarily attributable to a deficit in the sex glands, the gonads themselves, and sometimes to a deficit in the pituitary gland's gonadotropic stimulation of the sex glands, with or without various other complexities. In either case, the long-term treatment is the same—namely, replacing the sex hormone that is missing. In boys, the result of treatment is a perfect imitation of nature when the fault is attributable to the sex glands, but is frequently much less than perfect when the fault is the pituitary's. It is particularly difficult to get good growth of facial and body hair in the hypopituitary cases, so the complexion often looks juvenile and is a source of embarrassment.

The pituitary makes many hormones. It may fail to make only one of them, or many. When only the gonad-stimulating hormone is missing, then the individual is affected in physical sexual maturation, but not in statural growth. When growth hormone is also missing, the individual is not only sexually immature, but also a hypopituitary dwarf. If other pituitary hormones also are missing or deficient, then various other symptoms may be added to that of sexual infantilism. The resultant syndromes are of infrequent occurrence and do not present any essentially new issues in sex education and counseling.

The psychologic problem of pubertal failure with attendant immaturity of appearance is essentially a problem of avoiding as much as possible a discrepancy between chronological age and social age, despite the retardation in physique age. The problem is particularly difficult when dwarfism is also present, for then the individual has the additional handicap of a retarded height age to which people react unthinkingly—as though the person so short must still be socially a child.

The entire problem of psychologic development in pubertal failure, even under treatment, is made more complex by reason of personality traits and individual psychodynamics. It is quite possible that some forms of pubertal failure carry a predisposition to psychopathology. Some individuals with severe personality disturbance do not improve after obtaining an excellent somatic response to hormonal replacement therapy. It is not uncommon to find people who so resent the indignity of their condition that they try magically to restore themselves to normality by repudiating the medical help offered them or by discarding their medication.

Conversely, there are other people who have the psychological capacity to rise above their adversity, who keep up a dating and social life, despite their sexual infantilism, and who may even get married and perform coitally. Such people are examples of what the lucky personality trait of self-confidence can do. Some also exemplify the little-known fact that sexual thoughts, images, and dreams, as well as sexually arousing visual and narrative sensory materials, can function in a somatically infantile male who has attained the age when the biological clock of hormonal puberty normally comes into action. The presence of androgen itself is not in all cases an absolute prerequisite for this aspect of eroticism. However, androgen greatly increases the frequency of erotic arousal and the intensity of the genitopelvic component, which, in some cases, is nonexistent without the hormone. Androgen is a libido hormone for females also.

Sex education for sterility (see pp. 18, 20, and 33) is one of the special issues to be dealt with in the counseling of virtually all people with pubertal failure attributable to pituitary gonadotropic insufficiency.

Gynecomastia

Gynecomastia, or breast development in a male, is an anomaly of sexual differentiation that has already been mentioned in connection with hermaphroditism. It also occurs in otherwise normal males, having its onset with puberty (Plate 28). Breast enlargement may be small and transient or large, as in a pubertal girl, and irreversible. It is a source of mortification to the boy concerned, unless by some extraordinary coincidence he also has a gender-identity disorder and wants to be a girl. Its deleterious psychologic effect may be widespread and difficult to displace, even after successful plastic surgery to make the chest flat again. Sex education should include reassurance that breast enlargement is not automatically a sign of other feminine traits or tendencies to come. Its cause it is not fully known.

Hirsutism in Girls

Though the full and detailed story of the control of hair growth and baldness has not yet been scientifically ascertained, it is known that androgen plays a major role. Androgen permits the masculine pattern of body hair to develop within the limits set by hereditary type. The female body, if exposed to excessive amounts of androgen, will grow excessive body hair distributed in the masculine fashion (Plate 29). An extreme example is found in the untreated congenital adrenogenital syndrome of female hermaphroditism (Plate 30). In the old era before cortisone treatment, individuals affected with this hyperadrenocortical condition grew up to look like an exaggerated Mr. Atlas on a muscle-man magazine cover. There are lesser degrees of this same hyperadrenocortical condition which have their onset in adolescence or adulthood instead of childhood. These lesser conditions can also be relieved by cortisone therapy.

The cortices of the adrenal glands are not always the abnormal source, as in the adrenogenital syndrome, of excess androgens. An abnormality of the ovary itself may be responsible. In one type of abnormal ovarian function, the Stein-Leventhal syndrome, the ovaries are enlarged with cysts. Girls with this condition develop amenorrhea, missing their periods at the same time as they become hirsute. Both symptoms can be relieved by surgical reducation of the size of the enlarged ovaries. Menstrual failure is a usual accompaniment of androgen excess that is severe enough to produce considerable hirsutism. There are, however, many other sources of menstrual failure, including primary amenorrhea and functional or psychogenic amenorrhea. Hirsutism itself is not invariably of androgenic origin. In some instances, it may be an hereditary trait.

It is much more difficult to get rid of hair growth than it is to induce it. The afflicted girl is best advised to undergo electrolysis, according to the modern, not the old-fashioned, technique, regardless of what help she may expect from corrective medication or other treatment. In addition she will usually need special counseling to help prevent serious disturbance of social and personality development.

Chapter Eleven: Anomalies Of Gender Identity

For the majority of the human race there is no discrepancy between any of the variables of sex. Gender identity differentiates in agreement with assigned sex and with the somatic variables of sex, all of which agree with one another. In the case of hermaphrodites, where discrepancies may exist between the several variables of sex, there is usually concordance between the assigned sex and the gender identity. This concordance is nowhere better illustrated than when two individuals of the same diagnosis are differently assigned, the gender identity in each case differentiating in accordance with the assignment and rearing (Plate 31).

Concordance between sex of assignment and gender identity is not, however, a universal rule. Psychosexual identity may become established in repudiation, or in partial repudiation, of an assignment which the person interprets as an error. Ambiguity of identity is especially likely to result, in the case of an hermaphrodite, when the parental attitude toward the child's sex is ambivalent, and when the physique and uncorrected genital appearance evoke teasing or remarks of doubt or astonishment, especially from age-mates. An ambiguous gender identity does not necessarily correlate with the chromosomal, gonadal, morphologic, or hormonal sex. Sometimes the correlation exists; sometimes it does not. It is just as likely that a genetic female hermaphrodite with ovaries will have been ostensibly raised as female and want to change to male as vice versa (Plate 32); and correspondingly for a male hermaphrodite.

There are some lucky instances when a definite gender identity does not become established. In such a case, it will be possible to rehabilitate the individual in the other sex, maintaining coital adequacy and reproductive fertility. Thus, it is intellectually and emotionally rather satisfying to most medical specialists if a female hermaphrodite, assigned and partly reared as a boy, wants to change and to live as a girl, rather than if the same individual, raised as a girl, wants to be reassigned as a boy. Nonetheless, there is no point in insisting on the continuance of an unwanted female assignment—or in imposing a female reassignment—when, as a girl, the patient will, irrespective of anatomy and reproductive function, retain a masculine psychosexual identity and fall in love with another girl. The same principle holds true in the corresponding case of a male hermaphrodite.

In male hermaphroditism there are some lucky cases in which the individual rejects a masculine assignment and does not develop a fully masculine psychosexual identity. These are the cases in which the penis will remain forever unfunctional in coitus because of its underdeveloped, clitoral size, whereas, after surgical and hormonal feminization, the individual will function adequately as a female.

The most expeditious rule to follow is that no child after the toddler age should have a sex-reassignment imposed on the basis of an a priori principle. Every case should be individually evaluated and decided upon its own merits.

The most controversial type of case for sex-reassignment today is that of the transvestite transexual (Plates 33A & B). The transexual is a person who is typically, though not invariably, morphologically and physiologically normal according to contemporary methods of biological testing and measurement. He (or she) is, however, a quite extraordinary person, psychologically. No amount of reading can substitute for a direct personal contact with one of these patients in order to appreciate what they are like and to comprehend fully how totally different they are from normal members of their sex. They are driven by a fanatical desire to impersonate and also by a fanatical neglect of, and wish to be rid of, the sexual appurtenances of their bodies as given by nature. They want their bodies to look like, as well as be dressed like, the other sex, and they want to live the life of the other sex, occupationally as well as erotically.

The etiology of the condition is, to all intents and purposes, unknown. The life history and psychodynamic history are quite variable, except that transvestite desires to impersonate usually begin in early childhood. The response to psychotherapy or any form of psychologic therapy is poor. The most common form of "treatment" is arrest, trial, and imprisonment. Surgical and hormonal sex-reassignment is an ameliorative treatment, still at the investigative stage, which, in the majority of a hundred-odd cases known to have been so treated, has made life a little easier for the patients and, indirectly, for society also.

Transexuals know what they want and have usually ascertained, from reading and hearsay, a vast amount of sex education pertaining to their condition. Counseling is best directed toward rehabilitation and the day-by-day realities of living in the sex of new assignment. The parents or closest kin need counseling, since they usually have long been bewildered by their relative's condition. Brothers and sisters or other juvenile kin who will need to meet the patient under a new name and sex will also need counseling along lines similar to those appropriate to hermaphroditic sex-reannouncement or reassignment (see p. 63).

Postoperatively, transexuals are able to have satisfactory sexual relations as members of their newly reassigned sex. In males, the skin of the penis is not detached from the body. It is used, along with part of the skin of the scrotum, to make a lining for the newly opened channel of the artificial vagina. The sexual sensitivity of this skin, together with other sensitive tissue in the genital area, ensures the continuance of pleasurable erotic feeling. If the patient's hormonal substitution treatment includes not only estrogen, the female hormone, but also progestin, then the capacity to reach sexual climax will be retained. Progestin is actually a synthetic pregnancy hormone of the type used in some varieties of birth control pill. Physiologically, it acts as pregnancy hormone does in the normal woman's monthly cycle, but in biochemical structure, it resembles androgen, the libido hormone for both sexes.

In the surgery of female transexuals, the internal female organs are removed. Externally the clitoris is preserved. It is imbedded into the base of the artificial penis that is constructed from a skin graft cut from the abdominal wall. The procedure is complex, requiring several operations before the tube of skin hangs down in the position of a penis. The urinary tube inside the penis is made from a segment of the small intestine. The penis cannot become erect, but needs to rest in some form of support to ensure penetration of the partner's vagina. Orgasm is triggered from the region of the clitoris and is partly dependent on the continuance of male sex hormone treatment.

The partners of postoperative transexuals usually know the medical story of their mates. These partners have seldom had previous contacts with homosexuals or the "gay" world. They do not feel like homosexuals, because they judge their transexual partners by their personality and behavior, not by their anatomical history or sterility.

In addition to problems of masculinity and femininity, there are many other psychosexual anomalies of development which in themselves rightfully constitute the subject matter of a book completely independent of this present one. Some of these anomalies relate to parentalism as well as romance and copulation.

Chapter Twelve: Procreative Sex Impairments

The hidden assumption implicit in a good deal of the philosophy of sex education is that all teenagers are highly fertile and must be protected from their own capacity to breed. However, the sad fact of the matter is that many of the students in a sex education course, although quite normally developed for their age, may sooner or later have to come to terms with injury or disease that impairs or destroys their reproductive capability. The catalogue of such pathology is far too extensive to be dealt with here. Moreover, nothing would be gained by an attempt at complete coverage, since selected examples illustrate the main points.

Impotence

A weak sexual drive, accompanied by slowness to be sexually aroused and little sexual interest of any type, is the natural disposition of some individuals, just as is its opposite of satyriasis in the male and nymphomania in the female. Impotence is not a failure of sexual drive, nor of sexual arousal, but of sexual performance. In the male, it means failure either to obtain or to hold an erection. The loss of erection may occur before or after ejaculation. When ejaculation occurs, it is sudden and premature, before either the male or his partner is ready for it. In many cases of impotence, there is no organic lesion or deficit indentifiable by currently available diagnostic techniques. The loss of erection, particularly in premature ejaculation, is therefore considered to be functional. The recommended treatment is usually psychologic.

Not all forms of impotence, however, are psychodynamically functional. There are certain diseases, like sickle cell anemia, leukemia, the Leriche syndrome of occlusive vascular disease, and diabetes mellitus, in which impotence is a common symptom. Diabetic impotence may be relieved by treatment with androgen or gonadotropin. Irreversible impotence, without loss of ejaculation and the feeling of orgasm, may be a residual of an attack of priapism, the inability to lose an erection (Plate 34). It is very painful, usually of unknown cause, and almost always results in destruction of the spongy tissues of the penis as a result of coagulation of blood in them. Thus, the mechanism of erection by inflation of the spongy tissues with blood is permanently destroyed.

Chronic impotence, in the sense that sexual thoughts, feelings, and desires cannot produce an erection, is also one of the sexual aftereffects of a spinal injury that completely severs the nerve fibers of the spinal cord. If an erection occurs, it is by way of a low spinal reflex, without conscious sensation or erotic feeling of erection. Sexual life is essentially terminated by such an injury, which also produces paraplegia—that is, paralysis of the lower limbs, loss of sensation in them, and loss of elimination control. The paraplegic patient does not suffer quite the same pangs of mortification at being unable to satisfy his sexual partner as does the man with postpriapism impotence. The paraplegic loses most of the feelings and sensations of genitopelvic sexual drive as a result of his injury, but the man who is impotent after priapism does not. The latter, therefore, has his ego wounded time and again by having to stop sexual play after achieving his own orgasm, without being able to penetrate the vagina so that his partner may also reach an orgasm in the manner she likes best.

Frigidity

The female counterpart of impotence is frigidity. The term is often used to apply to women who are cold in the sense of having very little sexual interest or responsivity of any type. It is also used to apply to women who manifest a capacity to enjoy seductive flirtatiousness and the preliminaries of love play, but who "turn off" and become coldly unresponsive in the coital act itself. The frigidity may be so extreme that it will manifest itself as a temporary scissors-like locking of the legs, making intercourse impossible. More usually, it is simply an inability to abandon oneself to the movements and enjoyment of sex and an inability to work up to the climax of orgasm. As in the case of impotence in the male, frigidity may be psychodynamically functional, and is probably so in the majority of instances. It may also be attributed to an organic lesion, as in some cases of hormonal failure and paraplegia.

Loss of Organs

The sex organs may be lost as a result of traumatic accident or by surgical removal as a therapeutic necessity, especially for cancer. In the male, the prostate gland may be removed either for cancer or, especially in older men, because it enlarges enough to block the urinary flow. Removal for cancer is a radical surgical procedure in which destruction of nerve fibers may be inevitable. The result may be permanent erectile impotence. The capacity to feel the sensation of orgasm may or may not be retained. There are some postsurgical cases in which erection and the feeling of orgasm remain, but no fluid is discharged—the dry-run orgasm. Loss of the penis also does not destroy the capacity for orgasm, provided androgen levels are normally maintained. It does, however, destroy morale as a result of incapacity to satisfy the partner. Loss of the testes, by removing the source of male sex hormone (except for adrenal androgens), sooner or later diminishes libido, though not inevitably abolishing it completely. Sterility is an invariable result. Libido can be restored by androgen injections or pills.

As a consequence of their morphology, the external organs of the male are more prone to injury than are those of the female. Some women, however, do require radical removal of the skin around the entire pubic area because of skin cancer. These women do not necessarily lose their sexual feelings, though they may discontinue sexual relations through fear of injury. In the case of female hermaphrodites, it is fairly common to remove the enlarged, masculine-looking clitoris. Despite the importance of the clitoris as a focus of erotic feelings, its removal does not abolish the capacity to reach orgasm and does not, so far as one can judge, reduce the feeling of sexual gratification.

In the female as well as the male, it is remarkable how much erotic tissue can be removed without loss of erotic pleasure and the capacity to reach a sexual climax. There is good evidence of this fact in the erotic functioning of postsurgical transexuals, male or female. In neither case does erotic response disappear nor, in the majority, does the capacity to experience orgasm in the new sexual role, provided their hormonal prescription is correct.

The vulnerability of the female is internal rather than external, especially with respect to disease of the uterus and resultant hysterectomy. Some surgeons are far more conservative than others in undertaking this operation, and some are more attentive than others to the psychologic preparation of their patients for the loss of an organ by which their genealogical purpose in the world is defined. Hysterectomy, provided the ovaries are left intact, does not destroy the internal hormonal rhythm of the body, even though menstruation can no longer occur. Nor does hysterectomy impair sexual desire and response, including orgasm, except indirectly as a result of an adverse emotional reaction to the loss of the uterus.

Loss of Fertility

Fertility may be lost not only as a result of the loss of the organs of fertility, but also through their functional impairment. Some causes of infertility are rare; by contrast, others are more common. Thus, it is well known that mumps in adulthood may, in some men, so inflame the testicles and elevate their temperature that all the sperm cells will be killed, producing permanent sterility. Male fertility may also be indirectly impaired as a consequence of impotence. Male infertility may also be the result of an inability to ejaculate, even though no impairment of erection exists.

In females, infertility may be the result of the failure of the ovary to produce a mature egg during the monthly cycle of hormonal function, even though there is no disruption of menstruation itself. In other instances, the hormonal rhythm may break down, producing failure of menstruation (amenorrhea). The cause and treatment of such conditions can be complex, involving hormonal and/or psychologic therapy. Female infertility may also be basically a problem of the implantation of the fertilized egg on the uterine wall or its ability to stay there successfully. Spontaneous abortion or miscarriage, like menstrual disorder, may involve hormonal and psychologic factors in its cause and treatment.

Both starvation and overeating of extreme degree, either alone or associated with other symptoms in special syndromes, have a direct influence on the hormonal cycle and fertility. In severe starvation (for example, among prisoners of war), the gonads fail to secrete sex hormone, and the body undergoes various degenerative changes characteristic of starvation. Sexual function and desire disappear and are supplanted by desire, fantasy, and talk of food.

Starvation may be imposed by famine, or it may be the consequence of self-initiated fasting. An example of the latter is anorexia nervosa, a disease of obscure and complex etiology of pubertal onset chiefly in females. It may lead to death from an addiction to not eating. In its advanced stages, sexual functioning may fail to develop or, having developed, may disappear.

The converse of starvation is addictive eating and obesity. The cause of addictive eating also is obscure and complex. It may involve a metabolic abnormality, a neurological defect in the brain (especially the hypothalamus), disturbed psychodynamics, singly or in combination. Obesity may be associated with other syndromes, or it may constitute a syndrome of its own. There is not, therefore, a simple, straight-line relationship between obesity and diminution or loss of sexual function. The general trend, nonetheless, is that gross obesity is accompanied by sexual failure. In some cases of childhood obesity, the onset of puberty is delayed. In boys, the immature penis looks even smaller than it is, being retracted beneath a heavy layer of fat padding. Usually there is no identifiable "glandular condition" as is often believed to be the case in medical folklore.

Painful Copulation

Sexual intercourse resulting in successful pregnancy may be handicapped or even rendered impossible by pain. In the male, for example, there is a rare and little-understood condition, Peyronie's disease, in which the penis becomes deformed by the formation of internal scar tissue. It causes chronic pain which becomes intense when the penis erects.

In females, pain attendant on sexual intercourse is called dyspareunia. Dyspareunia is a symptom. The causes are varied, and a physical examination is always necessary to determine them. In some instances, surgical relief is possible; in others, pharmacologic, medical, or psychologic treatment is indicated. Dyspareunia may or may not be associated with painful menstrual periods.

Transmissible Genetic Defect

Some of the young people in any sex education group are fated to discover that they are the carriers of genetic defects that will show up in the next generation. They will not necessarily know of their fate, for many genetic defects—namely, those known as genetically recessive—are transmitted by parents who are hidden carriers. A parent who is a hidden carrier of a defect will not produce a child who is an open carrier of the defect unless the other parent is also a hidden carrier. When two hidden carriers are mated, there is for each pregnancy that occurs a 25 per cent chance of a child who will be an open carrier, a 50 per cent chance of a hidden carrier like the parents, and a 25 per cent chance of a child who will not carry the defective gene at all. A parent who is afflicted with defects or weaknesses that are genetically dominant may, regardless of the genetic status of the mate, pass them on to the offspring. There are various statistical probabilities of this type of genetic transmission, depending on the exact nature of the genes and chromosomes involved.

Once the probability of transmitting a genetic defect is known, whether prior to, or after the birth of, an affected child, genetic counseling is needed. Genetic counseling should begin didactically with information about the laws of chance as they affect the individual or the couple concerned. This kind of counseling appeals to the intellect. The emotions come next, for human beings do not make exclusively rational decisions on the basis of intellect alone. The final decision will be the product of the combined reason and emotion of both partners. The pedantic and cautious conservative will make a different decision than will the reckless gambler with fate. The genetic counselor cannot dictate the actual decision about breeding. He should not try. If he does, and if the unlucky couple disobey him or have an unplanned pregnancy, they will feel too guilty or ashamed to see him again for whatever further help they will need.

Chapter Thirteen: Conclusion

I is probably a good idea for all young people to have a brief acquaintance, in the course of their sex education, with the fact that genetic defects could cross their own path, with the fact that some of them may experience impairment of procreative function, and with the possibility that anomalies of sex may occur in the newborn and growing child. Forewarned is forearmed. Knowledge is prophylactic, whether in its applicability to oneself or to one's community of relatives and friends. Every young person will eventually hear, or know at close quarters, of at least one of the anomalies mentioned in this book. Moreover, though they do not need to hear the voice of a prophet of doom, young people develop in wisdom if they hear at least once that the exuberance of romance and the ecstasy of love and sex are not only a resolution of adolescent yearning or distress. They are also the beginning of the presentation of a fresh challenge to oneself, of unknown demands of fate, and of a new dimension of life to master.

Plates

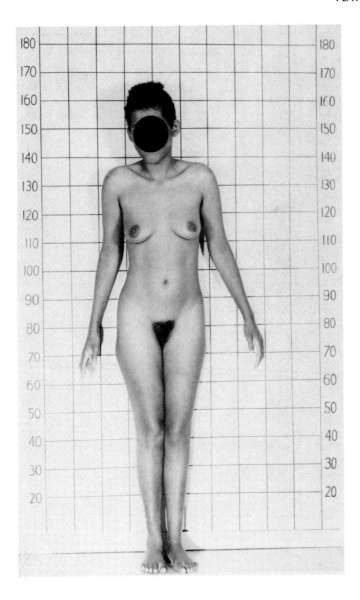

Plate 1.—Normal sexual morphology in a mentally retarded woman with the triple-X syndrome.

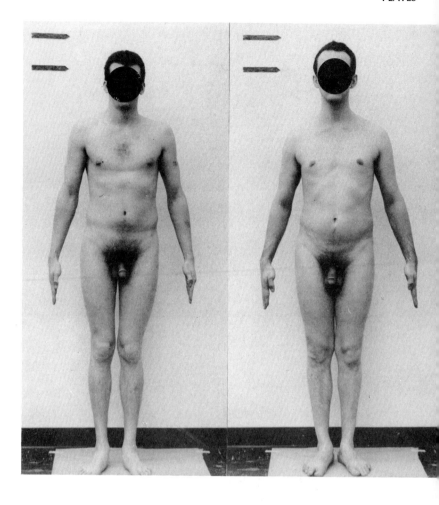

Plate 2.—Normal sexual morphology in two men with XYY chromosome
constitution. Heights 6'1½" and 6'2"; IQs Dull Normal; police
records in both cases (courtesy E. Philip Welch).

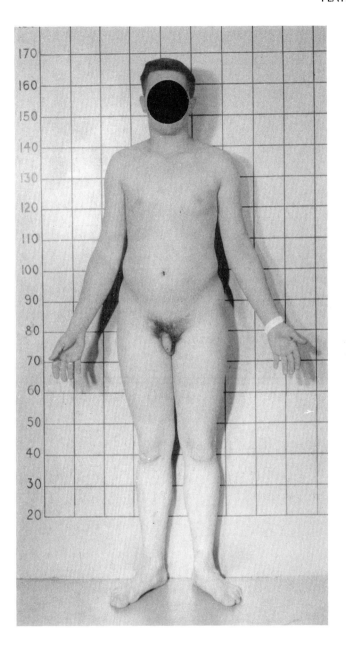

Plate 3.—Nineteen-year-old boy with Klinefelter's (XXY) syndrome. Note the breast development and hypogonadism.

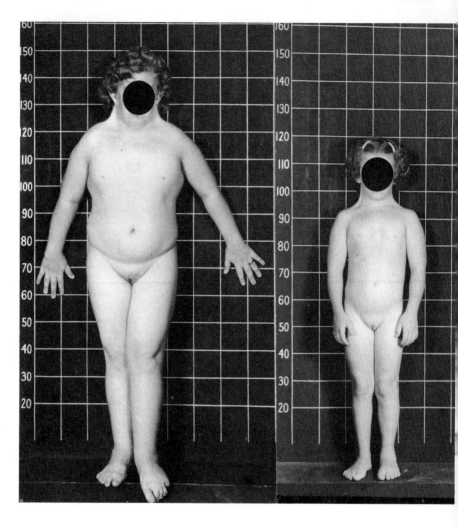

Plate 4.—Varying degrees of birth defect in two cases of Turner's syndrome with XO chromosome constitution. Note the short stature in both and the sexual infantilism in the older girl at age fifteen. The younger is ten and a half.

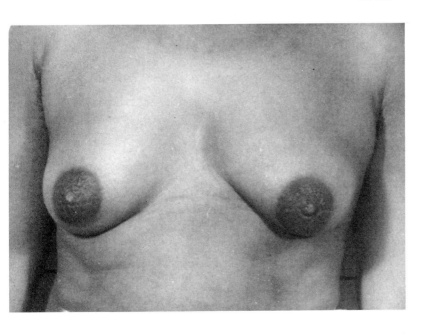

Plate 5.—Breast development as a sequel to estrogen treatment, beginning in teenage, in a woman of twenty-eight with Turner's syndrome.

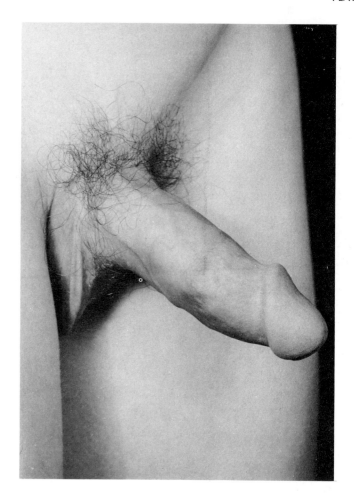

Plate 6.—A case of undescended testes in a young teenager. Note
the maculinizing effect of androgen on sexual hair and erectile potency.

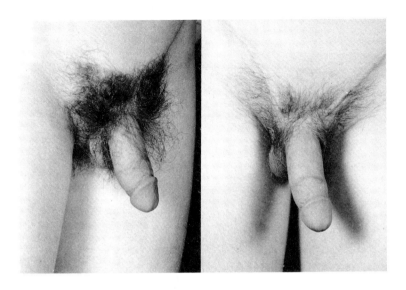

Plate 7.—Congenital absence of the testes (anorchia) before and after the surgical implantation of silicone prosthetic testes.

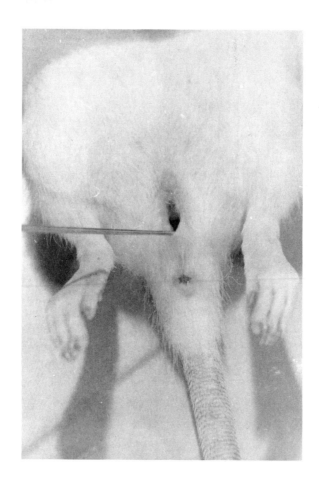

Plate 8A.—A genetic male rat with testes; the female external anatomy was produced by injecting the pregnant mother with antiandrogen, cyproterone acetate, 10 mg. a day from day 13 to day 22 of pregnancy. The baby was given another 0.3 mg. of the drug daily for 3 weeks after birth (courtesy, Friedmund Neumann).

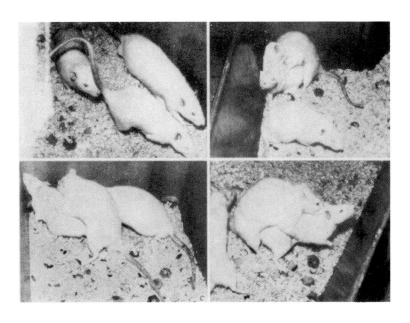

Plate 8B.—Mounting behavior of cyproterone-treated, feminized male rats subsequently castrated and implanted with ovarian grafts. Top left: The feminized rat is pursued by a normal male (note the steep rising of tail). Top right: Mounting attempt of the normal male is answered with defense reaction by the feminized male. Bottom left: Mounting attempt of the male rat is not answered with lordosis reaction by the feminized male. Bottom right: Mounting attempt of the male rat is answered with lordosis reaction by the feminized male (courtesy, F. Neumann and W. Elger).

Plate 9.—A newborn genetic female monkey with ovaries; the male external anatomy was produced by injecting the pregnant mother with the male sex hormone, testosterone. Arrow points to the penis, which is retracted, as it should be (courtesy, Robert Goy and Charles Phoenix).

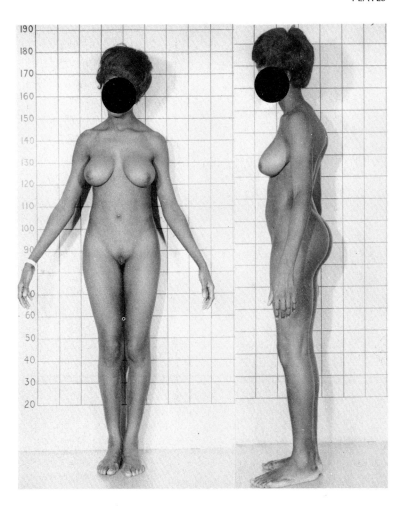

Plate 10.—A woman, technically a genetic male with two testes, with the androgen insensitivity syndrome. Note the absence of pubic hair. The gender identity and role are female. Breast growth is from estrogen, normally produced by testes in the male.

113

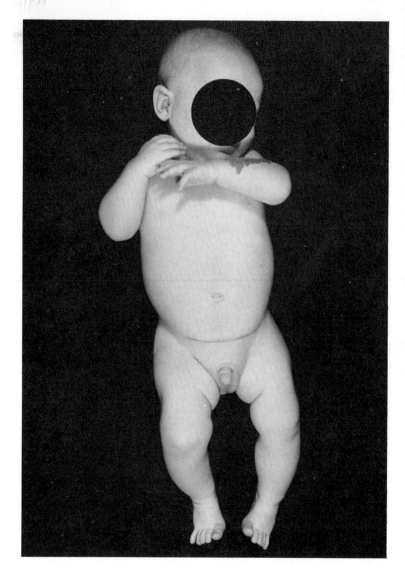

Plate 11.—Postoperative picture of a male baby in whom the uterus and fallopian tubes had developed to normal female size and needed surgical removal.

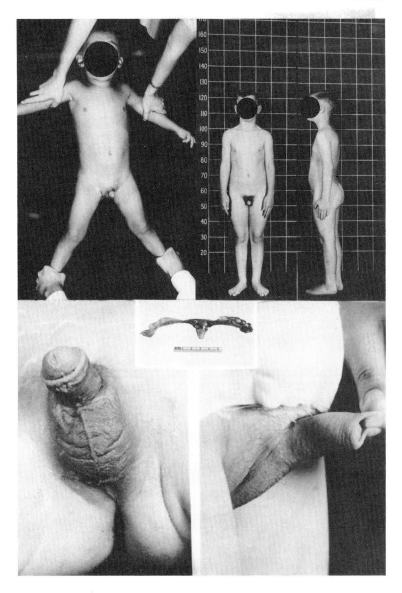

Plate 12.—Two cases of complete fetal masculinization in the
female adrenogenital (XX) syndrome with ovaries. Both boys continued
to live as males following diagnosis after early infancy.

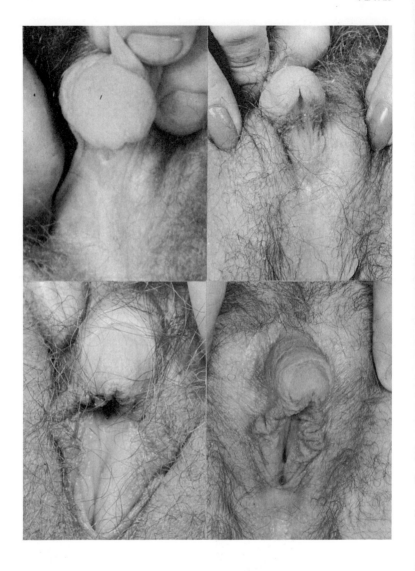

Plate 13.—External sexual abnormality in the uncorrected adrenogenital syndrome, showing four degrees of urogenital closure.

116

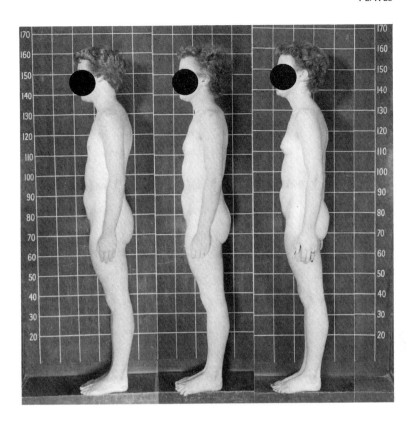

Plate 14.—The female adrenogenital syndrome of hermaphroditism, showing the effects of cortisone therapy on breast growth over a period of eighteen months. At right, aged eighteen years.

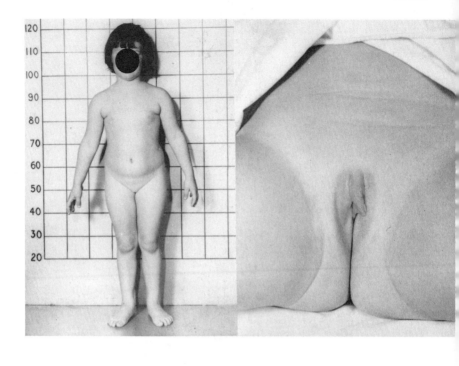

Plate 15.—Progestin-induced hermaphroditism in a female, showing clitoral enlargement.

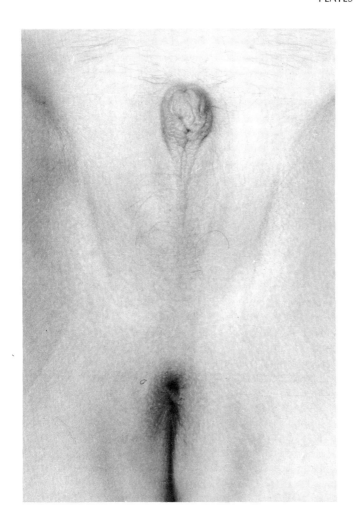

Plate 16.—Defective masculinization in a male hermaphrodite raised as a boy, who elected at age fifteen to be surgically and hormonally reassigned as a female.

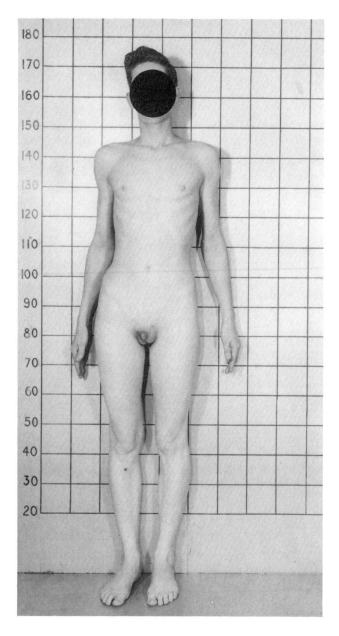

Plate 17.—Androgen insensitivity syndrome in a male hermaphrodite with a very small, surgically repaired hypospadiac phallus. Breasts have been surgically removed, as have the feminizing testes. There is an absence of aging as well as of virilization. Erection was impossible. Scrotum contains artificial testes.

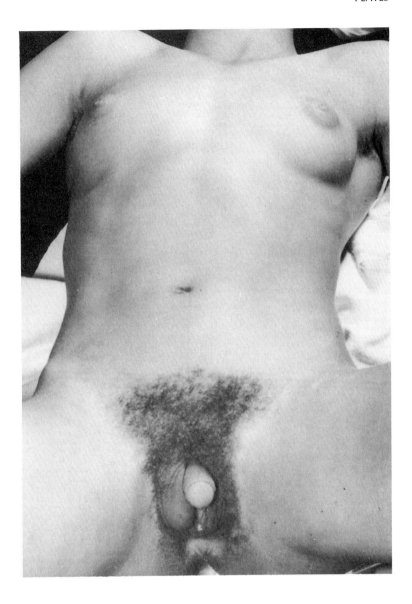

Plate 18A.—True hermaphrodite with left ovary, right testis and 44 + XX chromosome count; always lived as a male, married, and a stepfather.

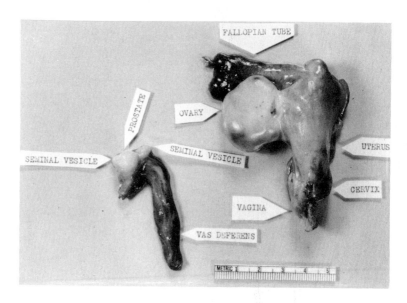

Plate 18B.—The internal organs of both sexes found in a hermaphrodite at surgery.

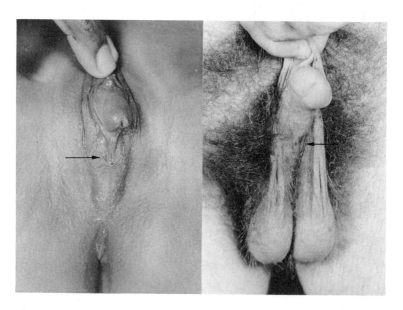

Plate 19.—Left, an extreme degree of hypospadias in a male, creating an external hermaphroditic appearance. The testes are undescended. Right, a lesser degree of hypospadias. The arrows point to the urinary openings.

122

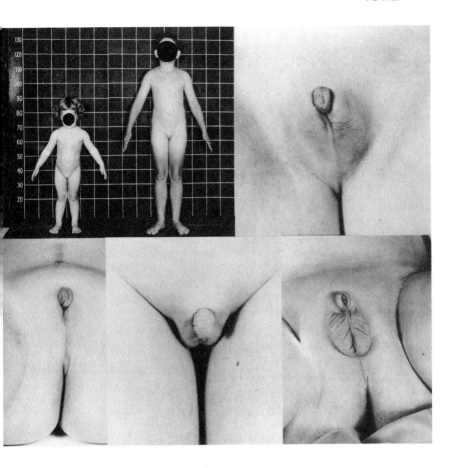

Plate 20.—The sex organs in four cases of agenesis of the penis
(microphallus) and the full view of two of the patients; one (left), surgically
corrected to be reared as a girl, and the other (right), raised as a boy.

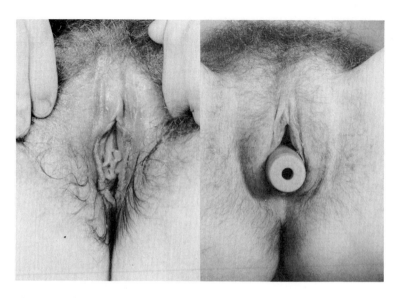

Plate 21.—Two examples of vaginal atresia showing, left, the normal external appearance and, right, the placement of a form after surgery for lengthening a too short vaginal canal.

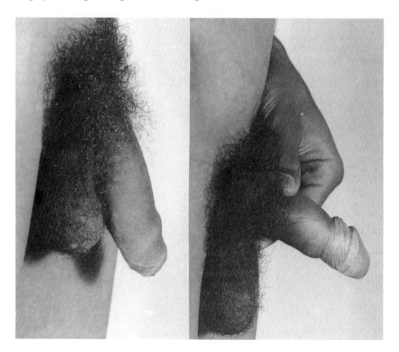

Plate 22.—Phimosis made evident when the skin of the penis is retracted.

124

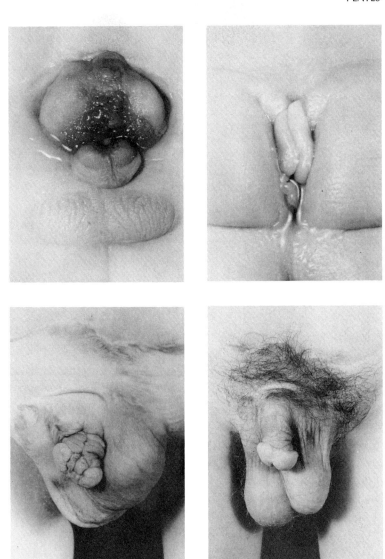

Plate 23.—Epispadias at birth, with congenital malformation (extrophy) of the bladder in a male (top left) and a female (top right). Below are two stages of surgical repair in the same male, at ages seven and fourteen.

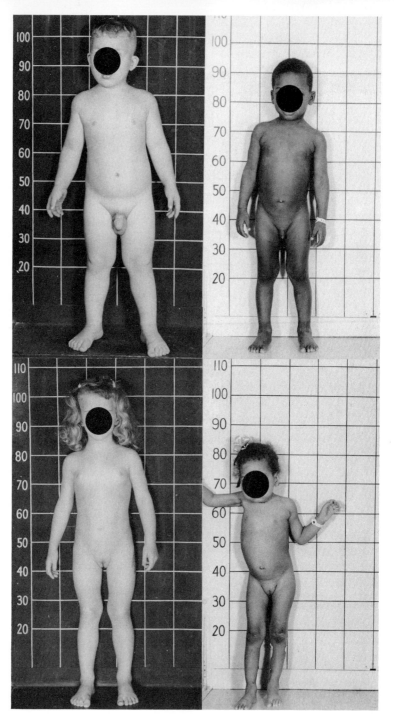

Plate 24.—Four children, all aged two and a half years, two with early sexual maturation and two without.

126

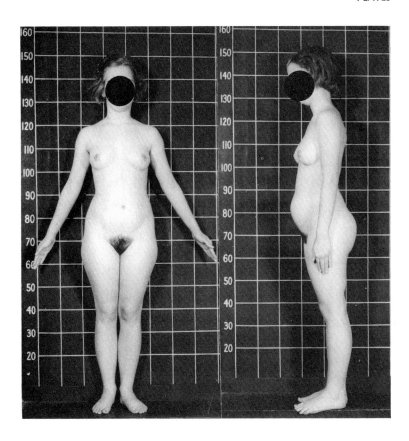

Plate 25.—Idiopathic sexual precocity in a girl nine years old, whose sexual development was first noticed at age six.

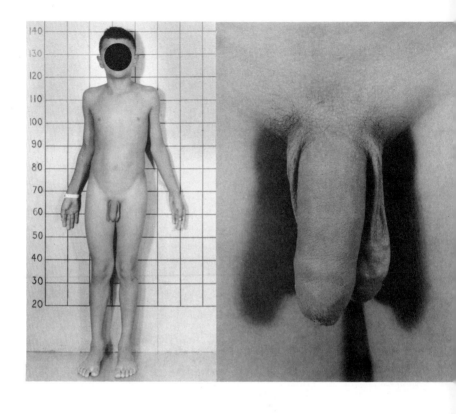

Plate 26.—Early sexual maturation in a boy aged seven with the male adrenogenital syndrome.

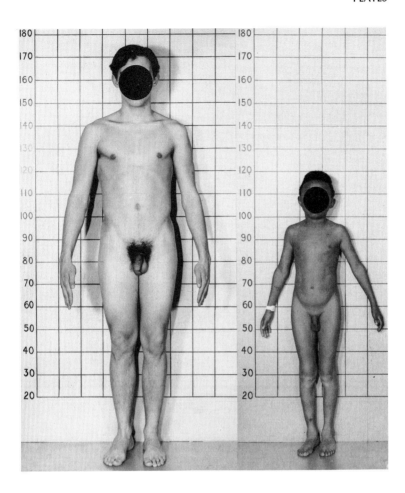

Plate 27.—Two boys aged seventeen; right an extreme case of hypopituitary pubertal delay (before treatment) in a boy also retarded in statural growth because of a deficiency of growth hormone from the pituitary gland.

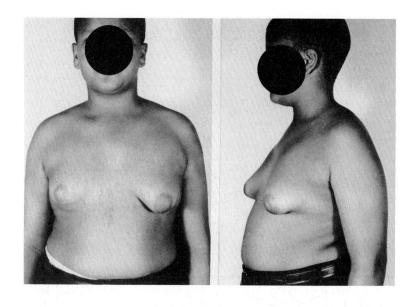

Plate 28.—Spontaneous breast development in a boy aged thirteen, prior to corrective surgery.

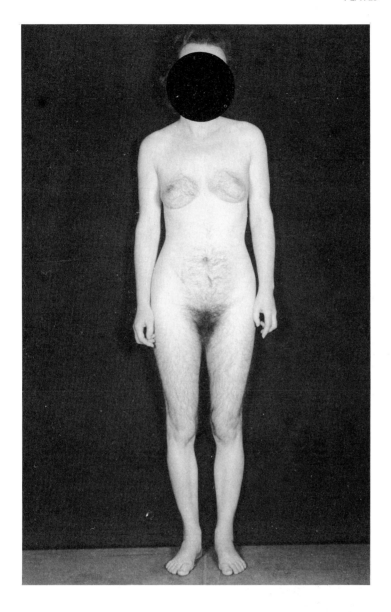

*Plate 29.—An extreme case of hirsutism produced by a
masculinizing tumor of the adrenal gland.*

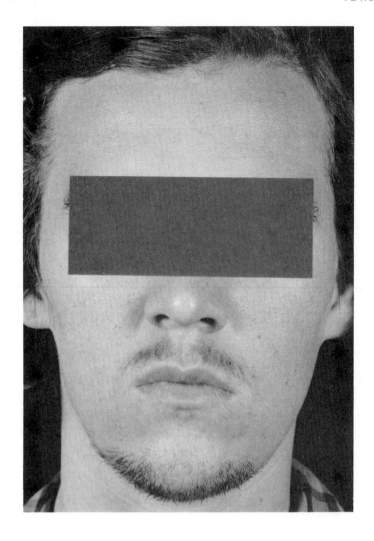

Plate 30.—Masculine hair growth in a girl of sixteen with the adrenogenital syndrome of female hermaphroditism, untreated.

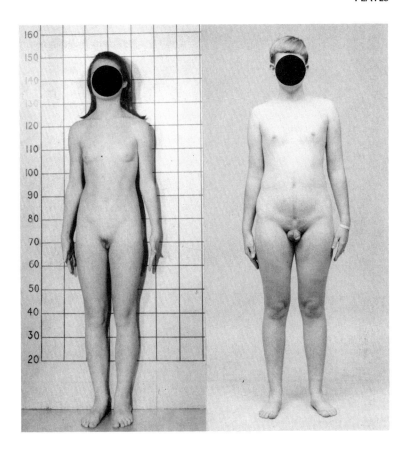

Plate 31.—Two people with the adrenogenital syndrome of female hermaphroditism, but with different assignment, rearing, surgical repair, and hormonal regulation. Each has a psychosexual identity to agree with the rearing. Note the artificial testes in the boy.

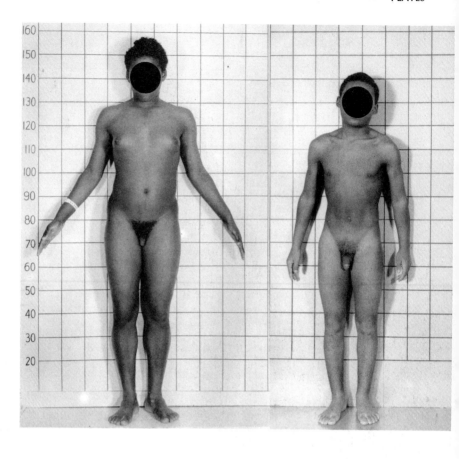

Plate 32.—Two people with the adrenogenital syndrome of female hermaphroditism. By age twelve, each had elected a reassignment of sex in order to settle the uncertainty in which they grew up. They are seen here after reassignment with different hormonal regulation and before the sex organs of the girl, left, were surgically corrected.

134

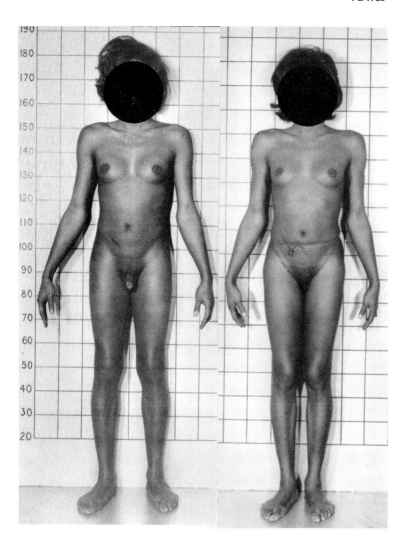

Plate 33A.—A male transexual, before and after surgical reassignment as a woman. The breasts developed as a result of female hormone therapy. On the right, a belt keeps the vaginal form in place.

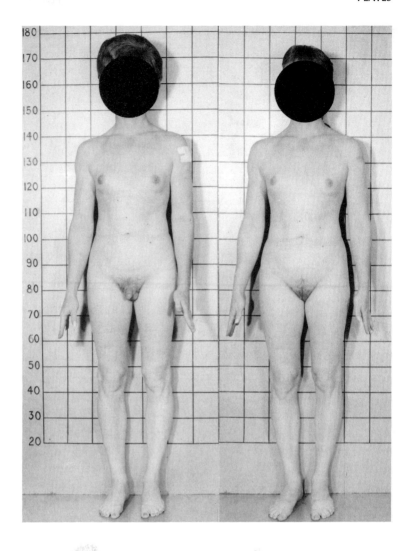

Plate 33B.—Another male transexual, before and after surgical reassignment as a woman. The breasts in this patient also developed as a result of female hormone therapy.

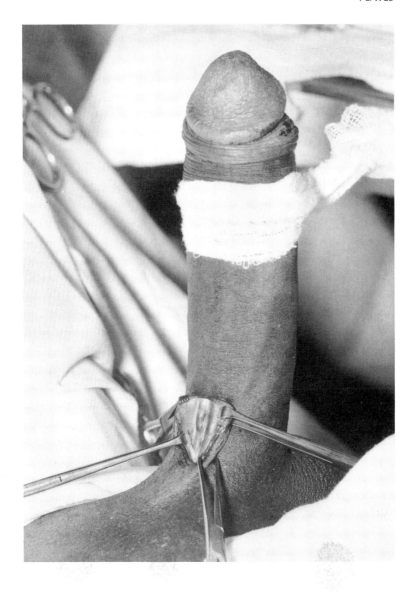

Plate 34.—Priapism is the inability to lose an erection. It is painful and requires surgery, after which the power of erection permanently fails in almost all cases.

137

Suggested Reading

Bartalos, M., and Baramki, T. A. *Medical Cytogenetics*. Baltimore: Williams and Wilkins, 1967.

Gardner, L. I., ed. *Endocrine and Genetic Diseases of Childhood*. Philadelphia: W. B. Saunders, in press (1967).

Jones, H. W., Jr., and Scott, W. W. *Hermaphroditism, Genital Anomalies and Related Endocrine Disorders*. Baltimore: Williams and Wilkins, 1958.

Money, J. Influence of hormones on sexual behavior. *Annual Review of Medicine* 16:67–82, 1965.

Money, J., ed. *Sex Research: New Developments*. New York: Holt, Rinehart and Winston, 1965.

Neubardt, S. *A Concept of Contraception*. New York: Trident Press, 1967.

Overzier, C., ed. *Intersexuality*. London and New York: Academic Press, 1963.

Wilkins, L. *The Diagnosis and Treatment of Endocrine Disorders in Childhood and Adolescence*. 3rd ed. Springfield, Illinois: Charles C Thomas, 1965.

Index

Designed by Gerard A. Valerio

*Composed in Optima with Optima display
by Monotype Composition Company, Inc.*

*Printed offset by Universal Lithographers, Inc.
on 70 lb. Patina*

Bound by L. H. Jenkins, Inc. in G.S.B. S/535 Sand #4